THE HOUND & THE HORN

Classic Tales of Moorland Hunting

William Frederick Collier

The text of this work first appeared in *Harry Terrell: A Dartmoor Philosopher* (1896) and *Country Matters in Short* (1899) by W.F. Collier 'Hunting in the Moor Country' is taken from *One Hundred Years on Dartmoor* by William Crossing, 1901.

This edition first published in Great Britain in 2000
Copyright © 2000 Simon Butler
Introduction © 2000 Freda Wilkinson
Copyright © on historic photographs remains with the named archives and individuals

British Library Cataloguing-in-Publication Data
A CIP record for this title is available from the British Library

ISBN 1 84114 051 1

HALSGROVE
PUBLISHING, MEDIA AND DISTRIBUTION

Halsgrove House
Lower Moor Way
Tiverton, Devon EX16 6SS
Tel: 01884 243242
Fax: 01884 243325
www.halsgrove.com

Printed and bound in Great Britain by MPG, Bodmin, Cornwall.

FOREWORD
by Freda Wilkinson

The central part of Dartmoor is still known as the Forest of Dartmoor. This meant originally that it was a Royal hunting preserve, not necessarily thickly wooded, and subject to Forest Laws to protect the venison (the beasts of venery) and the vert (their environment). In fact it was almost equivalent to a modern nature reserve or to a National Park as the term is understood in America or Africa. As Manwood wrote in about 1600, it was 'privileged for wild beasts and fowls of forest, chase and warren to rest and abide there in the safe protection of the king for his delight and pleasure'.

It is unlikely that Royal hunting parties had much effect on the wildlife population in such forests, particularly the more remote ones like Dartmoor, and kings could afford a certain chivalry towards their quarry which the commoner, after game to fill an empty larder, or to protect his crops or livestock, could not. But the Norman Kings certainly used to travel far with retinues of servants and retainers, to stay or probably 'camp out' on their Royal manors, of which Dartmoor had a few, and to receive such customary tribute as a couple of hounds or some arrows from the lords of neighbouring manors. For example Scorriton (near Holne) and Drascombe (near Whiddon Down) had to supply their sovereign lord with 2 arrows each when he came hunting in their neck of the woods.

Principal 'beasts of the Forest' were the red deer, the wild boar and the wolf, none of which would be popular with the husbandmen, living in or close to the Forest. In 1354 the 'Black Prince' ordered his foresters 'at calving time' (of the red deer hinds) to 'make lodges in their bailliwicks and live continually on the moor so long as the calves were tender, to save them from the herdsmen in charge of the cattle'. And in 1371 the Prince of Wales complained that 'about 100 dwellers round the Forest had hunted in the Forest without licence, took away deer, made divers assaults on his men and servants appointed to keep the Forest, and so threatening them in body that they dare not attend to the said keeping'. Apparently the men of Dartmoor were not particularly overawed by Forest law, and in time the deer were more or less exterminated. The organisation of Forest law finally fell into decay in the mid seventeenth century.

In the eighteenth century the first packs of foxhounds were established. Several Devon packs hunt on Dartmoor, the Dartmoor Foxhounds on about a hundred square miles of the southern moor, the South Devon Foxhounds in the south-east quarter, the Mid-Devon have the north-east country and Spooners and West Dartmoor Hunt the Tavistock/Okehampton side. They meet up in the middle at Postbridge.

Riding to hounds on Dartmoor is not for the faint-hearted and fit active and clever horses or ponies are essential to negotiate at speed the rough, steep going, and the stone walls, where the tumbled-down gaps are often the trickiest obstacles owing to the clitter of fallen rock on each side. Most unnerving of all perhaps is getting across the 'vane' or fen – the blanket bog of the higher moor where the only course is to jump off and lead one's horse, in single file, carefully, after the only person, perhaps a local moorman, perhaps a way-wise member of the hunt staff, who knows the only possible path. One such, I remember, was named, rather appropriately, George Baskerville!

Childe's Tomb beside Fox Tor Mire is a reminder of a hunting man who, centuries ago, lost his way home in a snow-storm and perished in that fearsome bog. Another man remembered when one passes Fox Tor is Arthur Piper, who, after the last war was kennel-huntsman and whipper-in to Mrs Mary Douglas-Pennant, M.F.H of the Dartmoor Hunt. Piper broke his neck hunting at Brimpts and Mrs Douglas-Pennant wrote afterwards – 'we put Arthur's ashes on a stone in Fox Tor. Mr Burt, the parson, Mrs Piper, Charlie Pengelly and I. In the moonlight I blew "Gone Away" on a horn and it echoed all over Fox Tor, perhaps the most marvellous thing any Master could do, and perhaps the hardest and best I ever blew too. The next week the fox and hounds went over that stone – never before and never since. Only Charlie and I had that cold feeling. No one else knew.'

Mrs Douglas-Pennant was one of the best-loved characters amongst Dartmoor folk of my generation, though her 'Hold Hard' put the fear of God into any thruster she considered might be discomfiting her hounds.

But it would fill a book to write of all the great and extraordinary and amusing characters who have graced the Dartmoor hunting scene. There was George Templer of Stover who founded the Dartmoor Foxhounds in about 1800 and who built, or caused to be built, the Haytor granite railway, and was described by contemporaries as a poet, wit, and scholar of great intellect. Mr Claude Whitley of Hedge Barton, Widecombe-in-the-Moor, was Master of the South Devon for 42 years (1938–1980), his father, Mr William Whitley having been Master for 15 years previously.

Mr 'Willie' Poole – the R.W.F Poole, who now writes regularly and most entertaining for *Horse and Hound* and the *Weekend Telegraph,* was Master of the Dartmoor for a few years in the 1960s.

Tom French of Widecombe was a well-remembered fox-hunting man, mentioned by Crossing in his *Hundred Years on Dartmoor.* He, Tom, was first employed by the farmers to get rid of the 'varmints' that were killing their poultry and their lambs, but he later took it up as a sport with the South Devon Foxhounds. His grandson, another Tom French, who was an estate worker at Spitchwick Manor said, in 1941, when he was 92, that his grandfather was very fond of hunting 'A proper foxhunter,' he rode to hounds on his white donkey – he never had a horse, he wore a red coat, given to him by the Master, Sir Henry Seale, who hunted the hounds kept at Holne Cot. Sir Henry gave up the Mastership in 1866.

There was a little boy, not so long ago, whose grandfather farmed above the River Dart near Holne and whose father was the farrier in the district, who developed his skills as a horseman by following the Dartmoor Hounds on his pony. He never had a riding lesson in his life, but he won the 'Dartmoor Pony Derby' cup at Chagford when he was about 10, and, in 1989 he rode 'Little Polvier' to victory in the Grand National steeplechase.

Yes – Jimmy Frost who runs a training yard at Hawson Stables with his parents; and he still enjoys his hunting over the moor. Hawson, lying between Holne and Buckfastleigh is close neighbour to Brooke Manor where in the seventeenth century the wicked Squire Cabell was said to hunt black hounds of hell by night on the Abbot's Way.

I remember a winter evening when the moon was full and the frost was coming crisp and hound music rose from the Dart Valley – Shakespeare's 'sweet discord' echoing and re-echoing from the steep woods on each side of the river. Only a couple of hounds hunting late on their own, and from the opposite hill came the urgent and plaintive notes of their huntsman's horn as he called them away, back home to bench and trough. But still voices pealed, like the legendary Whisht Hound themselves, through the moonlit woods.

So, throughout history the huntsman's horn and the cry of hounds has echoed over Dartmoor and drawn together in the heat and dangers of the chase the squire; professional men and women glad to throw off for a few hours the cares of office, surgery, or finance; girls and boys let loose from school; and the old-style country-man for whom fieldsports have always been his joy and release from the careful complexities and back-breaking labour of the 'simple life'.

In the green wood, beside the singing river or over the wild wastes the curse of Adam was for a space forgotten and memories left of great days, to be taken out, and counted over, and told to one's children's children.

CONTENTS

Foreword 3

Acknowledgements 10

Introduction 11

Author's Preface 13

Chapter One 15

Chapter Two 21

Chapter Three 29

Chapter Four 39

Chapter Five 49

Chapter Six 87

Chapter Seven 97

Chapter Eight 105

Chapter Nine 111

Chapter Ten 117

Chapter Eleven 123

Chapter Twelve 127

Chapter Thirteen 137

Envoi 145

Acknowledgements

Thanks are due to Freda Wilkinson for the Foreword to this edition, to Pauline Hemery for alerting the publisher to the works of William Collier, and to Peter Hamilton-Leggett for providing, from his excellent archive, original texts, notes and pictures.

INTRODUCTION
by Simon Butler

The politics of hunting has polarised public opinion. For many their antipathy also extends to much of the historic literature of country life – a great pity at a time of crisis in the countryside, for reflection on the past is an essential ingredient in planning future directions. Besides, some of our greatest authors have used hunting, and characters from the hunt, to populate their writings – are these now *persona non grata*?

Harry Terrell, whose story is told in this book, was a real person. Through Collier's biography we a given a portrait of a man who, in any age, would stand out from among his fellow men. That Terrell's natural habitat was the hunting field is quite suited to his birthplace and time, and that the strength of his character should survive the better part of two centuries places him, though little known, among the best company of English countrymen.

William Frederick Collier (1824–1902) was the son of a Plymouth MP, born into a family who were held in high regard for their philanthropy. William ran the family firm of Collier & Company, corn, wine and spirit merchants, later moving to Sampford Spiney, near Dartmoor, where he continued his public service and became a prominent member of the Dartmoor Hunt. It was here that he came across Harry Terrell.

Collier also wrote on a wide variety of subjects for a number of periodicals, including the *Saturday Review*, from which the later chapters of this work are taken.

Dan'l Leaman one of the great Dartmoor characters in the Terrell mould. As Robert Burnard says in the caption his 1888 photograph, he was 'not innocent, it was said, of a little poaching.'

AUTHOR'S PREFACE
TO THE ORIGINAL EDITION

I had the good fortune to know well two most amusing men of the West-country – Harry Terrell, and William Robert Hicks of Bodmin. They were both wits, but they wore their wit with a difference. Hicks told stories, which he studied, and told them in a dialect well got up. He was also a musician, and sung the songs of the country. He was more of a professional wit than Terrell.

Terrell was a child of nature, and never studied anything. He also told stories in a most amusing manner, but he told them as they occurred, and never took the trouble to embellish them. Every word he said, in the most natural way, was amusing and witty. If you met Hicks, he fell to telling stories. If you met Terrell, his telling, as he called talking, was on any passing subject of the most amusing and witty quality, with a good story now and then perhaps, but possibly of a finer order without them.

I have published *Hicks, of Bodmin** in the hope of preserving some of his sayings. And I now publish *Harry Terrell, of Dartmoor*, with the same hope – that two such characters may not be lost for ever. As an every-day companion Terrell was superior to Hicks.

* *Tides and Sayings of William Robert Hicks, of Bodmin.*

The South Devon Hunt, Manaton Green, 1924.

Chapter One

HIS PHILOSOPHY

Harry Terrell was one of the most amusing of men. He was both intentionally and unintentionally amusing. Intentionally, because amusement was the philosophy and object of his life. Unintentionally, because he was himself a very eccentric person without knowing it, and carried on his pursuit of pleasure, or amusement – to him those words had much the same meaning – utterly regardless of other people; though no one knew better that other people were essential to the pleasure and amusement that he sought.

He had a peculiar faculty of being the same to everyone, whether a peer or a beggar, and if the peer or the beggar did not see the matter in the same light, so much the worse for them, they would assuredly lose some of the amusement afforded by our fellow-creatures in this world. In such cases, which of course at times occurred, Harry Terrell passed them by on the other side, and they troubled him no more.

No man was better aware that the tongue is the grand organ for amusement, both by its direct and indirect functions, and being endowed by Nature very largely with the qualities of perception, memory, and wisdom, otherwise judgment, he turned, this organ – called by some the unruly organ because they know not how to manage it – to the best account. His perceptions were of the quickest and keenest; his memory, whether of sight, sound, or otherwise, was of the most retentive; and his judgment concerning things in general, men, horses, and dogs in particular, was of the soundest.

As he found in the tongue his best tool for his purpose, without taking much thought in the matter, or bestowing much labour on it, he attained to a wonderful command of language, gleaned from all sorts of men not to say women, met with from childhood upwards. His own tongue was a Devonshire tongue pure and simple, which he never saw any occasion to change or alter; he took nothing from it, but he added to it whatever seemed to him fit to enrich it. He did not study language, nor anything else. He did not work to attain an object. His object was not work, but amusement, and to work at one time that he might amuse himself at another time more distant, was a sort of uncertain balancing of accounts with the world that did not suit his fancy. He had a wonderful collection of words at his command, culled from the talk of a great variety of people, which he used at his own sweet will, uttered. with the accent in which he was born and bred. His was not a vulgar Devonshire, as it is heard in towns where the middle class delight in long composite words and a bastard accent, but a purely natural and native use of every word that came in his way, uttered in a purely natural and native tone. Every word in use among the Devonshire folk was at his command, consisting of a very rich and strong tongue in itself, not choice, not fastidious, not refined or superfluously delicate, but expressive in the extreme. This tongue will be for ever lost soon, to be changed into the Board-School English sent out by the Committee of Council on Education as the authorized Government Speech of the people.

Harry Terrell was a talker, or, as he called it, a teller, of the first water, and a good many other things besides. But as he was not ambitious, he did not talk himself into notoriety beyond his own native West. Many a great man has talked himself into his exalted position, but as exalted positions would have been tedious to Harry Terrell, he talked with no other object than to please himself, and, as talking is of necessity a social art, to please his friends. His talk, every word he said, had an amusing flavour in it, whether he was in a serious or a gay mood; it took him into a great variety of company, and he was the same man wherever he found himself.

The natural man in him would not put up with any, the least shade, of superiority, nor was there ever the slightest air of superiority in himself. Without having any opinions on the inequalities to be found in the world, avoiding such notions as not amusing and too serious to be worth his while to think about, he went into the world the equal of anyone in the matter of enjoying himself. No one could be a friend of his, and enjoy his talk, if he was not treated as an equal. This was no pretence of equality, but a sheer love of the fun and amusement that any inequality would tend to spoil. He was thus, for the sake of his talk and other fine qualities thrown into many various and different forms of society, and from them all gleaned the words and phrases that supplied him with a truly astonishing collection of material for talk. He had words on the tip of his tongue from the fireside of a small public-house in the depths of Dartmoor, where the native speech is in full force; or

"From the fireside of a small public house in the depths of Dartmoor."
The Forest Inn, Hexworthy 1888.

from the dinner table of the country gentleman, where he met men and women of high rank and good manner. He was rough and ready, as far as that phrase has any meaning in it that gives no offence. But as he was highly amusing to ladies, and very polite without troubling himself about his manner, the rough part of it was of no account.

For example: A fine old country squire of rather old-fashioned polite ways met him on the road, and asked for the pleasure of his company at dinner on Thursday next, or whatever the day was.

He replied, "I'll be there to foce the telling for ee." He knew he was asked to talk, and he promised to *force* the talking for his friend, which he was sure to do.

The old gentleman looked rather taken aback by the answer, and sent his kind regards to Mrs. Terrell. He was a bachelor, and it was to be a man's party, but politeness required a message to the lady, which Harry Terrell quite understood.

The answer the old gentleman got was, "I'll put all that to rights for ee."

The contrast between the old gentleman's very polite speech, and the rough and ready answer, was fine in its way.

Harry Terrell's philosophy, though he never troubled himself about any philosophy at all, was, nevertheless, a very profound philosophy. It was the philosophy of making the very best of the world as a place in which to enjoy oneself, without spoiling the enjoyment by the pains to be taken in trying to find out what the world is, and what we are in it. It requires no mean qualities to set yourself to so become master of the world, and the men and women in it, as to get out of the whole all the enjoyment it can afford.

Harry Terrell was a very richly endowed mortal, and he bestowed all his gifts on the enjoyments of the world.

If any moralists should say that he ought to have bestowed them for the good of his fellow men, the answer is, that he did so. To work hard for any purpose whatever was not one of his gifts, especially if that purpose were so far off as to be out of sight, which is such a common case with your moralists. But his gifts were to amuse, and the vast number of people he must have amused in the course of his life, leaving behind him many lasting notions of amusement, give him a claim to rank among the benefactors of mankind. Not the least of these was that kind of equality among men, which was peculiar to Harry Terrell, that had its source in the freedom from restraint and in the good fellowship essential to amusement.

The great Philosopher of the principle of enjoyment may be said to be Epicurus, who has been put aside by the Christians in favour of the Stoics, as the joy of the Christians is, theoretically, not of this world. To be such a Stoic you must make great sacrifices for the sake of a future state of things, which is the Christian doctrine, though the Stoics themselves were all for bearing present evils in their own way. If anyone had told Harry Terrell that he was an epicure, he would have scorned the soft impeachment in language of a very high order of expression. It has been the fate of the doctrines of Epicurus, interpreted by the Christians, to have fastened on them the vices of the glutton. Harry Terrell was far too wise to indulge in anything whatever that would be likely to destroy his powers of enjoyment of other pleasures in the world. He liked them all, and would not sacrifice any for the sake of one.

It is time to give some account – just what is necessary to understand the man – of Harry Terrell's "havings," or "havage," a Devonshire word which may be used with better effect, in lieu of the scientific "environment."

"Tavistock is very much changed now. The Dukes of Bedford have made it one of the prettiest and nicest towns in the kingdom." Tavistock Goose Fair c.1910.

Chapter Two

TAVISTOCK

H E was born in Tavistock on the 12th of April, 1807, and his life may be taken for the present purpose to have been enjoyed for about fifty years.

These fifty years are about the first half of the nineteenth century, in round numbers, ten years up or down not being worth attention. Life led in the first half of this century must be familiar to all of us, by reading or tradition.

Harry Terrell was a Tavistock man, and he must himself give an account of what that means.

It so happened that I was riding a nice Dartmoor pony, on the occasion of some races on the Saltram race-course, and I offered this pony to a dealer for £25. The dealer looked the pony over and deliberately said:

"He would be worth the money if he hadn't got *Tavvistock* legs."

Tavistock is, or was, always pronounced by the natives, rightly or wrongly, probably rightly, Tavvistock, being on the river Tavy, corrupted from *The Avon* – *T'Avon*. In writing Devonshire words, I shall do my best to give the Devonshire pronunciation in ordinary English letters.

As Harry Terrell was by far the best judge of ponies I ever knew – it was one of his many specialities – I went to him; he was always at races, and for years acted as judge at Saltram, and asked him what was meant by "*Tavvistock*" legs.

He said shortly, "Term of contempt."

I asked him why, and he told me two stories, with his explanation of the curious fact at the end of them.

"There was a man," he said, "drowned under Okehampton bridge, and the people of the town were crowded on the bridge to see the body taken out of the river. Someone said, 'T'is only a Tayvistock man,' when they all went away, as much as to say, 'Is that all?'"

The second example was:

The famous Tom Phillipps of Landue, famous as a huntsman, a Master of his own foxhounds, and a Squire, was drawing a covert for a fox. One of his hounds threw his tongue, otherwise "spoke." A very well dressed officer from a regiment in Plymouth, looking spick and span in his red coat, breeches, and top-boots, seeing a pheasant get up before the hound, said:

"That's feather."

Soon after a fox broke covert, when Phillipps, turning round in his saddle, roared out at the astonished officer:

"Feather is it? you Tayvistock son of a – " (female hound).

Why this most charming of all animals should, like Tavistock, be a term of reproach, is one of the curiosities of human speech which may rank with Tayvistock.

I said to Harry Terrell, "Why should this be?"

His very short reply was, "They'm jilles." That is to say, all the neighbouring places were so jealous of Tavistock that they adopted Tayvistock as a word of contempt, in a vain desire to bring it down to their level.

About fifty years ago, this term of contempt was in use, and as Terrell was a Tayvistock man, he put it down to jealousy. It is a remarkable fact, and it is mentioned by Mrs. Bray in one of her novels, who tells another story to prove it.

Tavistock is very much changed now. The Dukes of Bedford have made it one of the prettiest and nicest towns in the kingdom, but fifty years ago there were certainly peculiarities about Tavistock, that might have given rise to the sort of jealousy alluded to by Harry Terrell. Tavistock was a very sporting place in those days. Every one in Tavistock was a sportsman, and still there is a sporting feeling alive and kicking amongst the people.

When Harry Terrell was brought up there, racing, hunting of all sorts, shooting, wrestling, cock-fighting, badger-baiting, etc., were the life and soul of the parish.

"Tavistock was a very sporting place in those days." A group of badger diggers and their terriers, Devon c.1910.

Tavistock is a large parish as well as a town, and in Terrell's time every lawyer and doctor hunted, mostly in red coats, and went out shooting, of course. The host of the Bedford Hotel kept a string of race-horses, which he trained on Whitchurch Down, and the race-course there. Some other hosts of inns had no less than 400 game cocks "out to walk." That is, sent out to different farms as cock of the walk, which caused them to be furious at the mere sight of another cock.

A very astonishing Tayvistock man, called Rubby, flourished about this time. Rubby was a very peculiar man, a well-known character, and he lived in the back slums of Tavistock, which no longer exist. He was a tall, lean, upright-standing man, looking about fifty years old, more or less. He was affected with a sort of shaking palsy, which caused his head to be constantly in motion. His hair was a very light brown in colour, and he wore long curls in ringlets, which fell below his neck, and were kept in a perpetual dance by the shaking of his head. The word weird is much used now, and he was the personification of it. He was a man of few words, hardly ever saying anything at all, but in many respects he was a most formidable person. He kept a few, three or four couple, good, hard, white small, broken-haired terriers, of the old fashioned sort, who would face anything, and were very pretty. They followed him everywhere. He carried a long ash-pole, about six feet in length, which, in his hands, was a weapon to be afraid of. He was a sportsman, always on foot, and appeared with his terriers whenever there was any fox-hunting, badger-hunting (a speciality with him), otter-hunting, fulmart-hunting, etc., going on; not to mention cock-fighting, and other now forbidden sports.

Rubby was a strange, remarkable character, with whom it was no joke to quarrel, for he had no fear of any sort, and could use his ash-pole or his fists with formidable effect, or could give a man a fall in the Devonshire style, without taking the trouble to say a word about it.

He was once seen, when out otter-hunting, crossing the river Tavy, near Tavistock, with one terrier in his mouth, another under his arm, a third in his hand, and the inevitable otter-pole or ash-staff in the other hand, wading to the spot where the otter had gone in.

He was always employed to clear the course at the Tavistock races, on Whitchurch Down, where there was, and is, a very good, and a very pretty race-course, much used for racing before the railways came to spoil local races, with other purely local things besides.

Rubby's peculiar ways were well displayed in his method of clearing the course. As usual in country races, the straight run in, the winning post, and the grand stand were in a well-selected part of the course, temporarily railed off on both sides with posts and ropes from the distance to beyond the winning post, to give room for the horses. When orders were given to clear the course, Rubby with his ash-pole walked in his long, slow stride, the whole length of the railed part, without uttering a word, his head and ringlets shaking as customary. If a toe or knee, whether of man, woman, girl, or boy, were inside the line of rope ever so little, down came the ash-pole on toe or knee with dread results. Rubby's way of clearing the course was most effective. Everybody knew there was not the slightest use in remonstrating, either in polite or strong language. Nothing was said by Rubby; if a toe, or a knee, or any part of the body for that matter, were on the course or inside the rope, the ash-pole was inevitable; no language or anything else was of any account to Rubby. To quarrel with him was no joke, as everybody knew well enough; and in his capacity of clearer of the course he was in office, backed by the "powers that be."

I was talking to a friend in the middle of the course at the races, when we saw Rubby coming along on one side, the people getting out of his way with the greatest anxiety. When he came to the end of the ropes on one side he would cross over and go back the other side, but it was never safe to have as much as a toe inside.

My friend said – "Here comes Rubby. We must get out of the way."

I said – "There is plenty of time, Rubby, knows us well enough, He won't touch us."

"Won't he, though!" said my friend, "I don't advise you to try."

And the course was clear of us.

Rubby's appearance on the course was enough. His

tall figure, his ash-pole, his long determined stride, the shake of his head, and his complete silence, acted like magic. There was a suspicion of a little madness in Rubby, which added to the danger of arousing his wrath.

Rubby was always ready to bet five shillings that he would "draw" a badger with his own teeth, without a dog or any help. A badger is a very formidable animal, and it is a test of very high courage in a dog to go in to a badger in an earth, or in a barrel, and draw him out. In Rubby's case, the badger would be put into a barrel large enough to be a sort of kennel or refuge for the animal, and Rubby would put his head into the barrel, his shoulders concealing what he actually did, and draw the badger out with his teeth. How he managed it no one knew, but if anyone was bold enough to bet the five shillings Rubby always won, with any badger that might be produced, not merely a tame one to win the bet with.

Rubby was always present on foot with his terriers at fox-hunting, otter-hunting, badger-hunting, or fulmart-hunting, especially the three last, when terriers are more in request.

Badgers are great diggers, and disturb a large space of ground in digging their extensive earths. On an occasion when some badgers, which had done considerable mischief by digging, were to be taken out at the place of the well-known sporting squire, Mr. Arthur Tallyo, of Stanleigh,* Terrell, Rubby, and a very sporting company were present. Rubby had put in one of his terriers at the end of a large earth, and had put his own head in after him to listen. At the other end of the earth it occurred to Squire Tallyo to try the effect of gunpowder, and he put a small charge into the earth as far as he could reach, with a train of powder leading out of it. He fired the train, and the explosion had the effect of blowing earth and stuff into Rubby's face and eyes, which were underground.

---

* *The real names, of course, not used.*

Tallyo stooped down to look into his end of the earth to see the effect of the gunpowder, and most unexpectedly felt a tremendous blow from Rubby's ash-pole on his back. He jumped up in a towering passion to face Rubby, who stood quietly by with his ashpole in a threatening attitude, his head and ringlets shaking as usual, his face showing the effects of the explosion, and his aspect singular, ghastly, and ferocious. Tallyo, who knew not fear, was proceeding to offer fight, when his friends took him aside to dissuade him with weighty arguments not to fight Rubby, who was a dangerous man to meddle with – no glory but much grief being likely to follow such a contest.

Tallyo gave it up with a bad grace, and sore shoulders, but the badger hunt was too tempting to be abandoned, and proceeded. Rubby was content with his one slash with his ash-pole, as well he might be, when he found there was to be no fight, and returned to his earth.

Rubby was a great feature in the Tavistock sporting world in Terrell's earlier days, when sport was a wild sort of affair. He was an older man than Terrell, and did not live to an advanced age.

Rubby was a *Tayvistock* man.

The Tavistock country was hunted, at that time, by William Morgan, of blessed sporting memory, Squire of Woodovis, not far from Tavistock. Tom Phillipps, of Landue near Launceston, a mighty hunter and huntsman; Newton, of Milleton, in the Okehampton district; and John Bulteel, of Flete (succeeded by Charles Trelawny, of Coldrenick), in the Dartmoor country, were all within reach, and were reached, sometimes, at great distances, by the Tayvistock sporting men, amongst whom were some very fine horsemen, Harry Terrell about the best.

Though I do not put Harry Terrell before the world as a sportsman, but rather as a Dartmoor Philosopher, a disciple of Epicurus without knowing it, supposing himself all the while to be a good Church of England Christian, as churchwarden of his moorland parish; yet, having been brought up in a sporting world, he was the best sportsman I ever knew, taking his remarkable knowledge of all sports into account.

His philosophy has been explained as the philosophy of the enjoyment of life, and he found that his sporting inclinations, or instincts, or whatever they are, gave him more of that enjoyment than anything else, not only for sport-sake, but for the taking him into jovial fellowship, in which his genial nature regaled itself.

Chapter Three

HE, HIMSELF

Harry Terrell was a first cousin of Jack Russell, otherwise the Rev. John Russell, the famous North Devon sportsman, whose mother was Nora Terrell, Harry Terrell's aunt. He married Margaret Edgcumbe, a daughter of a clergyman, a member of the well-known West-country family of that name, and his only child and daughter (who survived childhood) was called Margaret. He began life with the idea of being a doctor, and went into a chemist's and druggist's shop in Tavistock as a sort of beginning, not an uncommon introduction to the profession in those days. He used to tell of a black man who injured his eyebrow and was brought into the shop. Terrell had to apply brandy to the wound. The brandy trickled down the face of the patient into his mouth, which received it most willingly, the black saying, "Very good medicine, massa, do very much good."

He did not like the work, but he never forgot what he learnt, and was always an authority on doctoring. It is said, every man is a fool or a physician at forty; if so, he was certainly a physician.

After giving up the chemist business, he went to learn farming with a leading farmer near Totnes, which was much more to his liking, though sport was his chief attraction. He always farmed in a rough and ready sort of way, his power of observation making him a fine judge of beasts of all sorts. He knew so much about domestic animals of all kinds, their breeds, their habits, their wants, their defects, and their diseases, with the current popular remedies which he despised, that he would surprise anyone who did not know him with the extent of his knowledge, never putting it forward as any merit of his, but showing it by casual remarks.

"No veterinary surgeon allowed here," he used to say should be over the door of every stable. Those were the days of bleeding and physic, much changed for the better now.

I shall have to say a great deal about sporting, especially hunting, because Harry Terrell looked upon sport as a means of enjoying life, health, and good fellowship. He was no fisherman, because that sport was solitary. But this memoir is of Harry Terrell, the man, and not the sportsman, by far the most interesting, peculiar, and original character I ever met. He always farmed, and at one time took a farm, but sporting, hunting in particular, was his pursuit to attain to his idea of the enjoyment of life.

He had a fine, piercing, dark eye of great seeing power, his hair was black, and he had a handsome face with a nose slightly aquiline; not one of your great hooked noses, like those of the Jews, or Romans, sometimes attributed to our aristocracy. He was a good height and figure, not tall, and would have been classed as a middleweight.

He was always alive to everything that was going on – nothing escaped his eyes or ears – he was very quick, a great observer, and all was stored away in his fine memory for practical use at any time. By such means, without reading more than for his amusement, the extent and variety of his knowledge proved on occasions to be very surprising. It was not his way to display his knowledge, for he was singularly free of any care of what others might think of him, but to use it, and he never showed it except to use it. He knew enough about law to keep out of its way, and if he wanted an opinion he could ask the exact question that would bring forth the reply required. So with medicine, he knew enough to keep out of the way of doctors.

His wife sent for one, on an occasion when she thought him very unwell, and he said afterwards, in a half-mocking, half-humourous tone, that, being an old friend and the roads bad, the doctor charged him £2.2s. Those were in the £1.1s. days.

He was an excellent judge of cattle, sheep, and pigs; of horses, more than excellent; of hounds, which he judged at puppy shows; of dogs in general, but especially of terriers, in which he took great delight, and always had one or two good ones.

It has been said that Harry Terrell had no ambition. He did not seem to have an atom of that vaulting faculty, nor of self-conceit, nor of self-consciousness. His sole care seemed to be to enjoy himself, and to share his enjoyment with everybody else, making them in that way contributors to his pleasure.

I have followed him about in the hunting field, when the hounds were drawing a great covert, just to hear what he would say to anyone he met, especially if it were a stranger. Harry Terrell's object in that case was to put the stranger at his ease, to find out if he was a sportsman or any other interesting characteristic, and help him if necessary. Telling, as he called talking, was the soul of life. Silence was very far indeed from being golden to him – it was dullness and stupidity itself. He loved laughter, and provoked it wherever he went. There was not a word he said, on such an occasion, that was not either amusing in itself, or said in a way that made it so. If the stranger stared and gave himself airs, he was sure to have something said to him that made the whole field laugh. But generally a stranger used to hunting could see at a glance that he was "somebody" in the hunt, and would answer according to his hunting lights. All young men were "young feller" to him, and he delighted in *entering* them, as he called it, and if they were tractable, helping them. His perception was wonderfully quick, and I have heard good judges say that, as soon as he came to a field of horsemen, his eye was on the best horse there instantly. He could see at once, by his horse, his seat, his bridle and bit, the way his breeches and boots were put on, whether a stranger was a good sportsman, or only out for the various other objects than mere sport, which attract people to the hunting field. His first question would be put in a most friendly way, artfully contrived to find out by the answer how much sporting knowledge the stranger could show. I always found it well worth while to listen to what he said; the words, the phrases, the tone, and manner, were amusing beyond description. No one could have a faint idea of what Harry Terrell was who had not heard and seen him, his apparently careless way, his apparently careless seat on a horse, easy and good, and the lurking laugh on his countenance.

"He could see at once, by his horse, his seat, his bridle and bit, the way his breeches and boots were put on, whether a stranger was a good horseman."

His idea of riding was to let his horse alone. The reins, he said, were only to regulate the pace, and he was, on principle, a loose-rein rider. He was a great judge of pace, in hunting, in particular, but also on the race-course. To be a good judge of pace, up-hill and down-hill, especially in the counties to which he was accustomed, is an invaluable and not a very common accomplishment. To ride jealous, he called it "jillez," is fatal to riding to hounds. Every horse has his pace, and every run has its pace. In a short scurry it does not much matter what the pace may be, but no man knows what a short scurry may lead to, and to have a beaten horse, or a half-beaten horse, when the real run comes, is to be no sportsman.

Harry Terrell was also a great judge of condition, as he was of so many things besides, and he used to "conditionize " – another of his terms – his horses in a way peculiar to himself. His method was to ride his horses constantly on the moor. Idleness was the root of all evil, and a certain number of hours daily, on soft ground, at a slow pace, would "conditionize" a horse to perfection. He had no groom, but usually a man of all work. His bits, bridles, and saddles, were always clean, and told of the sportsman, but his horse was not groomed by a stud-groom. There was a sportsman-like, rough-and-ready look about the whole turn-out. He did not consider good condition in his horse accomplished till he had reduced him, by slow riding for many hours, to as low a state of flesh as was consistent with high feeding. By letting his horse's mouth alone, and riding him slowly for many hours on soft ground, the horse did not get off his feed, but ate ravenously in high health, and did not wear his legs. Harry Terrell's horses looked very lean, but in a long trying run, up and down steep hills, sometimes at a great pace, his would be more than likely to be the only horse on terms with hounds. I have seem him perform quite extraordinary feats in long, fast, and trying runs on his little horses. A slow easy gallop was his favourite pace, and I think he was right in preferring for his horse, especially going up hill and in soft ground, a slow gallop to a trot. A horse can use his hind legs with better effect in a gallop than in a trot, but it must be slow in unfavourable ground.

He could cure a puller or a borer better than anyone I knew. His plan was not to pull at them, which is easily said, but not so easily done. He would cure a puller, if he were curable at all – some horses, it must be acknowledged, are incurable – by riding them until they were too tired, and were disinclined to pull. He would take them out with harriers, and ride them for many hours, not fast of course, day after day, until they gave up pulling from sheer weariness. He would then bring them to his favourite way of riding with a loose rein, at any pace he chose. With his idea of condition, a horse was not likely to pull. To pull, to start, to buck, or to jump about, was a sure sign to him of want of condition. Some huntsmen's horses, if their masters were not too rich, and Harry Terrell's also, I have seen actually dull with condition, but not to be beaten in any run. Wealthy men go out hunting with two or three hunters, and second horsemen, the horses looking as perfect as the best of grooms can make them look, but they always look too well. It is generally said, that the two-days-a-week horse, and the two-days-a-week hound, will beat any others.

At the finish of a run once, when a good field of good men were well up, there was naturally a talk about horses. Someone said, that Lord Some-one-else, a well-known sportsman, had said, that "he never had a horse in his life that he really liked," of all the many horses which had gone through his hands.

"Ah!" said Terrell, "He's one of they discontented rich fellers.

That was of his Dartmoor philosophy.

He always knew the pace that the horse he was riding could go best and longest and was utterly devoid of jealousy, knowing very well that whoever passed him would have to come back to him if the run were worth seeing.

Young Ambition, as he called him, once passed him at a gallop with hounds up hill at the beginning of a run.

He called out with his usual good nature, "Gently, young feller, gently, you'll beat your horse."

"Oh!" said Young Ambition, "He's a hack, and I'll take my guinea out of him." (Hack-hunters were a guinea then, they are two guineas now, like doctors.)

"You've a took nineteen and zix pence out of 'un already," said Harry Terrell.

Which proved only too true, for the poor hack stopped soon after, hopelessly beaten for the day.*

He very much surprised me once, when riding a rough unpromising looking pony in the summer, with a party of ladies, up a long sloping grassy hill to the top of a Tor. The party were all galloping or cantering, and I looked at Terrell's pony going along at a slow gallop, every moment expecting him to subside into a trot, or walk, or to stop. But stop he did not, and kept up his slow gallop with Terrell, by no means a very light weight, to near the top of the hill, where the others stopped.

I said, "That must be a very good pony, Terrell?"

"I've been a husbanding of 'un up uncommon," said Terrell, not agreeing at all that he was wonderfully good.

I was much impressed then with what a man could do by "husbanding up" a horse, who knew how to do it.

Terrell, in his earlier days, kept a pack of harriers, and hunted anything that could be hunted.

It was usual, about seventy years ago, for anyone to keep a pack of harriers, who could; and every squire had his pack. Red deer were common in Devonshire in those

* *This true story was told in an article in the* Saturday Review *on 'Fox-hunting on Dartmoor', and afterwards in* A New Book of Sports; *the article appearing as Chapter 12 in this book.*

days, and a pack of harriers might rouse one, run him into the country of the next pack, which would then be put on the line, the scent of the deer being lasting and holding for an hour or so, and run him to the next pack, and so on, until he got back pretty safely to his own coverts in Exmoor. Fifty miles is nothing to a red deer, but a good deal for five or more packs of harriers, which, in those days, were harriers, and not dwarf fox-hounds, slow and disposed to be line-hunters.

Any pack of hounds and any game was acceptable to Terrell, and he gave up his harriers after a while to go out with any pack that suited him at the time. He was a bit of a rover in his way, usually within the limits of Devon and Cornwall, and liked change of country, change of scene, a variety of people, and change in the style of hunting. In his day, men rode very long distances to covert, and home from hunting – there were no steam covert-hacks. Rich squires kept their galloping-hacks, and if they had to go a distance would send one on a certain number of miles, besides their hunter, which was sent on the night before. Neither Terrell nor his cousin, Jack Russell, was one of these, and few men have gone the distances that they have on their hunters only. I have, myself, ridden with Harry Terrell twenty-five miles to covert, hunted all day, and twenty-five miles home again, he on the same horse all day, though I rode a covert-hack to the meet, to which I had sent on my hunter the night before. It is true, we had not much

"Terrell would have put up at any roadside inn at all suitable." The Ring of Bells, North Bovey 1894.

sport. If we had had much of a run, Terrell would probably have put up at any roadside inn at all suitable.

Terrell's setters were great rangers, and if they were not staunch when they found game, they were no good to him. His hawk's eye would follow them from his pony, and when they came to a point he would ride up to them, get off his pony, shoot his game, and ride on again, in that way covering a wide extent of moor.

He usually "summered" his hunters by turning them out, a by-no-means orthodox proceeding, now and then riding them slowly on the moor. He said they were the better for being in the fresh air, which is undoubtedly true, and if they had their oats, as they would have if in the stables, it made no difference in their condition; if anything, it was better to be out, the grass would not hurt them if they had their oats. He knew every little particular about horses, as before said.

Though short of horses, he managed somehow or other to hunt nearly every day in the season, either with fox hounds or harriers. He had many mounts given him, on account of his fine riding, and he often went out in a leisurely way, especially with harriers, merely to look on, and have a "tell." Instead of training and galloping his hunters, a task usually given to grooms, not much for a hunter's good, he rode them himself, giving them long hours at a slow pace, looking on at harriers. His hunter, and his pony also, were by this means always in first-rate condition for going, with not an atom of fat in their composition. He used to say that he never saw hunters in such condition anywhere as Dartmoor hunters were.

Terrell was fond of quoting the old Devonshire maxim – Never say Never – in which there is certainly much wisdom.

"Jack Russell was great a stag hunting on Exmoor, and hardly ever missed a meet." The Reverend Jack Russell c.1870.

Chapter Four

JACK RUSSELL
AND GEORGE TEMPLAR[1]

Russell himself, told me that he rode his horse a hundred miles into Dorsetshire on a Monday, to hunt with a friend – hunted all the week – riding some other horses, of course, and a hundred miles back to his parish on the Saturday. As he neared home, his horse, being weary, fell with him, not his first fall, nor to Russell's surprise. When Russell got up from his fall, a small boy who was walking on the road looked up in his face, and said very earnestly:

"I wouldn't ride he no more if I was you.

So much for a hunter of Jack Russell's, who never rode a bad one.

As I have brought Jack Russell on the scene, and as he was Harry Terrell's first cousin, it may not be amiss to say something more about so well-known a man.

Here is a letter from Jack Russell to Harry Terrell:

"DENNINGTON,

"January 31st, 1865.

"MY DEAR HARRY
"Do you remember that 'once upon a time,' you and I and a few more ran a fox from Bradford Wood to Bow and killed him? and do you also remember that I gave the head of that fox (wasn't he one of the right sort?) to the late George Owen? Well, whether you can or cannot remember the last circumstance, it was so, and now he is 'gone to the land from whence no traveller returns,' the head has been sent back to me by his nephew, William

---

[1] *The usual spelling is Templer. George was the son of James Templer who built the canal at Stover, near Newton Abbot.*

Owen Cooke. It is set up in a glass-case, and as you deserved a trophy of that fox more than any one who rode the run, I now write to ask if you will have it, for if you say 'aye,' I shall be delighted to send it to you. No one in this house will care to keep a fox-hunting trophy of mine after I am gone, therefore, by offering it to you – who earned it in reality – I am depriving no one of any gratification, but showing you that as

> *'We have seen a run together,*
> *And ridden side by side,*
> *It has bound us' (I hope) 'to each other*
> *Like a lover to his bride.'*

"The frost is going – hurrah! I am well horsed for close or open country, and hope I may yet see, what I have not seen so far, a good old-fashioned run before the season closes. My love to mother and daughter.

"Yours most sincerely,

J. RUSSELL

Jack Russell was a famous teller of stories, and he had a fine collection, especially some of another North Devon parson, to whose harriers, as a curate, Russell performed the office of whip. This Rector was fond of his tricks. Sitting, drinking gin and water with his guests one evening, they complained that the gin was rather strong.

"Too strong, is it?" said he; "watter it, then, watter it, don't ee see the kittle on the fire?"

As the kettle, however, had gin in it instead of water, he succeeded in making his company drunk.

On another occasion, this Rector had a trench dug across his yard while his guests were carousing, and as they left in gigs or on horseback, something the worse for his hospitality, he had the joy, to him, of seeing them all have a fall in getting over the trench. They knew him, and did the best they could.

The Bishop, Phillpotts, not approving of all he had heard of this same Rector, went to see him.

He was in his boots, spurs, and breeches, just going out hunting.

He speedily jumped into bed, and told his housekeeper to say he was very ill in bed with small pox.

The Bishop said he would call another day.

The Rector said the Bishop was "as ugly as a jackass, and twice as mischievous."

At a fair, a prize was to be given to the boy who could sit longest on a piece of wood with an edge made as sharp as possible. Of such are rural sports. The Rector told his stable-boy to sew a halfpenny into his breeches, and the boy won. This boy was a famous galloping whip afterwards, a hard rider, and was killed at a fence.

Jack Russell told me the following story of himself.

He was at Southampton, and had a second-class ticket for an express train to London. He settled himself down in the corner of his carriage, and, just as the train started, a man bustled in hurriedly and sat down with rugs and wraps. Russell concluded from his looks and behaviour that he had just landed from a ship as passenger from Australia. Those two had the carriage to themselves.

Soon after they left the station the weather came on very rough – hail, rain, and wind.

Russell, who was a talkative and sociable man, said, "This must be rough weather in the North."

"Why in the North ?" said the man.

"I was thinking at the time," said Russell, of the North of Devon.

Oh!' said the man, "that's where I'm going to."

"And what may your business be there?" asked Russell.

"Why, I'm come all the way from Australia," said he, "to horsewhip a man called Jack Russell, who lives there."

Russell was a tall, well-built, strong man, though getting old then. He said, "Perhaps he can take care of himself, and it won't be so easy."

"Oh!" said the man, "he is getting old now, and can't be equal to me. I have seen a good deal of hard life."

"Why do you want to horsewhip him?" said Russell.

"Because he horsewhipped me," said the man. "He keeps a pack of fox-hounds, or used to, a few years ago. I was a poor man then, and was breaking stones in a quarry. A pack of hounds came up to the edge of the quarry, and there they stopped. This Jack Russell came up, and cast his hounds all round. Then he comes up to me, and he says, 'Where's my fox?' I said I hadn't seen him. 'That's a lie,' he said, and cut me across the back with his whip, and he could use his whip, I can tell you. I shall go and serve him out. I never saw his fox, and knew nothing about it, but this Mr. Russell was in a terrible tear,* because he had lost him."

Russell said he remembered the circumstance very well. The hounds had brought the fox to the quarry, and neither they nor he could make anything of it afterwards. He did his utmost to find where the fox had gone, which in Jack Russell's hands was as much as could possibly be done, but could never even guess what had become of him.

The same thing happened to him on another occasion, in the middle of a road; and he found out afterwards that some gipsies had taken the beaten fox up and gone on their way with him, some little time before the hounds came up.

Russell was a great talker on all sorts of subjects, and turned the conversation on sheep-farming in Australia, with which the man had made his fortune, and on which Russell himself was a good authority.

The time passed very pleasantly, and the conversation of the man on sheep, wool, and farming in

---

* Tare, a Devonshire word.

Australia, was very interesting to Russell. They arrived at the Waterloo Station, and the man got out. Russell followed, and was just going to say good-bye, when the man looked into his face and said – "Will you dine with me, Mr. Russell, at the Langham?"

The man had known him all the while. He had seen the well-known figure at the Southampton station, familiar to him in days gone by in the North of Devon, quite irrespective of the whip, kind as Russell: was with a goodfellowship manner to all classes, the lowest included, and he had purposely jumped into the same carriage with his old countyman.

Russell said he never had a better dinner, and spent a very pleasant evening with the rich stone-breaker.

He told me he had once a very long tiring run with his hounds, not fast, for if so it could not have been long, and he ran his fox further and further from home; his field got tired and left him one by one, until he found himself alone with his hounds in a lane, all pretty well beaten, but he knew the fox could not be very far off At last the hounds turned in 'at a gate, and when he came up he saw the fox set up against the hedge quite beaten, and the hounds all lying down staring at him, too tired-out to kill him.

Russell went up to the fox and found he was so beaten that he could handle him, and he vowed he would not kill him.

He took him on his saddle and turned homewards; a very long way he had before him in the dark. He felt very much tired, and found the fox very troublesome to carry. At last he could bear it no longer, and he said he never felt anything more than when he made up his mind to throw this fox down to the hounds. But the fox was wet, his horse was tired and stumbling, his hounds were lagging along as if they had not had their rights, and he threw the fox amongst them in a fit of despair.

He always, he said, regretted killing that fox.

Jack Russell was great at stag-hunting on Exmoor, and hardly ever missed a meet. Stag-hunting is, or was, a speciality with North Devon parsons. It was bad form, among the farmers or anyone else, to have a christening, or a wedding, or a funeral, on stag-hunting days.

Jack Russell and Harry Terrell, the cousins, were very unlike one another in many respects. Harry Terrell could not have been a parson, nor could he have gone to Sandringham, nor preached before the Prince of Wales. He was no preacher, but a great talker, as Jack Russell was also, but the style was different.

They both rode very long distances in the old hunting days.

In his later days, Jack Russell liked to show young ladies, out with the stag-hounds, the short cuts and byeways, where they could come upon the stag or the hounds, or see the stag set up perhaps in the middle of a river amidst lovely scenery.

A charming young lady went to Exmoor for stag-hunting, and Terrell wrote to Russell to look after her, which he did. But her lover turned up also in the hunting field, and Jack Russell wrote to Terrell,

"The next time you send a young woman up to me stag-hunting, mind you don't send her sweetheart with her."

One Billy Black was the only man who ever could, and who ever did, deceive Jack Russell with a bagged fox. So well was the secret kept, that Jack Russell to his dying day never knew that the fox he ran at that famous meet, and killed, was a bagman.

GEORGE TEMPLAR

It was in the old country of George Templar on Dartmoor, now hunted by Mr. St. Maur's South Devon Foxhounds. George Templar was a mighty huntsman, and a gentleman well known and well beloved. He built Stover, afterwards bought by the Duke of Somerset, and now Mr. St. Maur's. George Templar hunted his own hounds, and no man understood bagged foxes as he did. With this slight allusion to such a man as George Templar I will give some verses written by him when he gave up hunting.

My Old Horn

Though toil hath somewhat worn thy frame
And time hath marred thy beauty,
Come forth, lone relic of my fame,
Thou well hast done thy duty.

Time was when other tongues would praise
Thy wakening notes of pleasure:
Now, miserlike, alone I gaze
On thee – a useless treasure.

Some hearts may prize thy music still,
But ah! how changed the story,
Since first Devonia felt the thrill
That roused her sporting glory.

Grace still in every vale abounds,
Yet one dear charm is wanting;
No more I hear my gallant hounds
In chorus blithely chanting.

And there my steed has found a rest
Beneath the mountain heather,
That oft like comrades sworn we prest
In pleasure's train together.

And some who at thy call would wake,
Hath friendship long been weeping;

A shriller note than thine must break
Their deep and dreamless sleeping.

I, too, the fading wreath resign,
For Friends and Fame are fleeting
Around his bolder brow to twine,
Where younger blood is beating.

Henceforth be mute, my treasured horn,
Since time hath marred thy beauty.
And I, like thee, by toil am worn;
We both have done our duty.
                    (Signed) G. T. 1833.

George Templar was very much esteemed, and although he was old when Harry Terrell was young, he had his influence on Terrell's life – his sporting life at all events.

George Templar was hunting with a great pack in the Shires, and, being a forward rider, he was up with the hounds when they came to a check. Neither huntsman nor whip being up, he cast the hounds; as he was so doing the huntsman came up in a bad temper, and, using language, said,

"Do you think you can kill a fox!" little knowing how many he had killed with his own hounds.

Templar turned round, and said to those who had come up, "He is quite right. I could not kill a fox with his hounds."

Fine characters die, and are forgotten; whilst others, less fine, live and figure in the pages of History. Even if they bungle or mar their country's fortunes their names become immortal, small men though they may be.

George Templar was great and well beloved in the life he chose.

Harry Terrell told me the story of the bagged fox with which Billy Black deceived Jack Russell. Billy Black, having been brought up under George Templar, knew all about bagged foxes.

Russell brought his hounds down from the North of Devon to have a week's hunting in the South, and there was anxiety to show so great a man sport. Fear was felt that there might be a blank day: foxes were more scarce in those days than they are now, and Jack Russell would not like to be brought down so far to run a bagman. Billy Black therefore undertook that he should find a fox. Billy Black, Harry Terrell, and a confidential man, were the only persons trusted with so delicate a secret. Jack Russell was known to be on such intimate terms with his hounds that the least variation in the behaviour of any one of them would attract his attention.

Of course there is a great peculiarity in the scent of a bagged fox: if he has only been captured for a short time he is not like a wild fox, and a great change has come over him which affects the scent he gives forth; to this a well-entered hound is certain to respond by a change of tongue and manner that could not escape such an eye and ear as Jack Russell's.

There was a very large and thick brake to be drawn, and the confidential man with the bag was instructed to lie down in the middle and thickest part of it. When he heard Russell's horn, on leaving the meet, about a quarter of a mile off, he was to let out the fox, and lie quite still and quiet himself, until everyone was gone, that no one might see him.

The hounds were thrown into one end of the brake, and gradually drew up to their fox, which they found, and Billy Black was there to view him away, and distract attention by a superabundant amount of hallooing. The hounds settled on their line, ran their fox well over a good galloping part of Dartmoor, and killed in the open. They eat their fox – I have known hounds refuse to eat a bagman – and Russell never knew he had been cheated with a bagged fox, thanks to Billy Black's cleverness, but always talked of it as a perfect run. He was never told. Those who knew it, who were few, were afraid of his mighty wrath. He did not like bagged foxes, and used to say that a fox which had been handled was no good for two years.

Harry Terrell used to say the same. He also said that a wild animal, very different from any domestic animal, if kept in confinement, even if it became comparatively tame, had always an expression in the eye, a sort of glistening, glassy look, which meant perpetual fear of its greatest enemy – man. Terrell was sentimental on this subject, and I have often observed, with a thrill of pity, the peculiar glassy look of the eye of a captured wild animal, a sign of the most dreadful of all our emotions – fear.

Chapter Five

NOTES AND TALES

Terrell was hunting in the North of Devon with fox-hounds, and sport not being good, he made up his mind to ride home to his wife, instead of waiting till the next day. He was living then at Ottery, a farm about six miles west of Tavistock, fifty miles from where he left the hounds at four p.m. He got home about two the next morning, put up his horse himself, and called to his wife at her window. She was used to this sort of thing.

These men of the olden time used to cover long distances by riding at a slow houndtrot, about the pace an old-fashioned huntsman used to take his hounds to their kennel, after a long day's hunting. It is a sort of jog-trot. "The right butterwoman's rank to market – for a taste:

> *"If a hart should lack a hind,*
> *Let him seek out Rosalind.*
> *They that reap must sheaf and bind:*
> *Then to cart with Rosalind.*
> *Sweetest nut hath sourest rind,*
> *Such a nut is Rosalind."*

This pace is very trying to the small of the back, to those who are not used to it. But if your horse is good at it, it is a very pleasant way of getting over a deal of ground at about five to six miles an hour. Few men knew better than those old hunting men what a horse can really do, when properly ridden. Terrell, with his hunter or two, has done great feats with a single horse, and some of the very best and toughest horses, famous in their time in the West of England, went through his hands.

Every sort of hunting was Terrell's delight, and he shot well likewise. His hunting and riding maxims were excellent. He knew fox-hunting, of course, as the chief of sports. Hunting the wild stag on Exmoor, so different from the carted deer, was also a favourite diversion of his, where he met his cousin, Jack Russell, who was great at it, and where he also could get cub-hunting in the month of September, on the bye days.

Much has been written, and much more might be written, about hunting the wild red-deer on Exmoor, which, in the month of September is as charming a sport as can well be conceived. Terrell was good also at hare-hunting, and when people talked of the craft of the hare, as they are apt to do, he used to say the hare was the greatest fool he knew. The craft for which she has had the credit being merely the accidents of her ways and of scent. Terrell was too good an observer to be taken in by old hunting lore.

Otter-hunting in the summer was a favourite with him, though he did not care to wet his feet for it. He liked to lounge on his horse by the river side and encourage the men up to their neck in the river, amusing himself and the company in general. He knew well how otter

hunting ought to be conducted, and the peculiarities of the animal. He used to say that otters bred all the year round, for there was not a month in the year in which otter cubs had not been found. Last, but not least in love, fulmart hunting was a joy to him.

The fulmart, short for foul-martin, is the fitch, or polecat, now almost extinct in most parts of England.

The fulmart, alas! has been civilized off the face of the earth, as his cousin, the fox, would be, if he were not hunted, by such highly civilized specimens of civilization as gamekeepers. There may be one or two fulmarts left on Dartmoor, but to find one and run him has been given up for many years as hopeless.

On Dartmoor this animal was well known as the fulmart in Terrell's time, and old sportsmen say it was the best game to hunt of all. Why, I cannot say, unless it was that it wandered long distances, and when found went straight for home, leaving a considerable scent behind it. It was fond of rivers, and the tongue of the otter-hound has sometimes been betrayed by it to tell a false tale. An old Dartmoor hand told me, that if you found a hole on the moor with the remains of frog's legs all round it, that was a fulmart's earth.

As a summer sport, Terrell and a few choice spirits used to take four or five couple of hounds to the "Saracen's Head" (the Buller crest) at Two Bridges, Dartmoor, to hunt the fulmart in the fastnesses of the moor, as Terrell used to call quite the wildest parts of Dartmoor, in those days seldom visited.

Harry Terrell went to stay with Billy Black, in his lonely cottage on Dartmoor, for fulmart-hunting. There was port wine to be had, of which Terrell, at least, was a good judge. They had to sleep in the only bedroom, with two beds in it.

In the middle of the night Terrell was awoke by Billy Black sitting up in his bed, cheering his hounds.

"As a summer sport Terrell and a few choice spirits used to take four or five couples of hounds to the 'Saracen's Head' at Two Bridges to hunt the fulmart." The Saracen's Head (Two Bridges), 1889.

"Ya-at! ya-at!" said Billy, "ya-at." Then of a sudden he sung out at the top of his voice, "Tally ho!"

"He's afoot, Billy," said Terrell, "He's afoot."

Terrell and Billy Black knew all about good living. Billy would get up early, catch a dish of trout, and cunningly fry them for breakfast in a frying-pan with butter, sprinkled over with oatmeal, fresh and delicious. Wishtman's Wood was not far off, and there they would begin their draw for a fulmart, over the bogs, to West and East Dart Heads, Fur Tor, Tay Head (Tavy Head), Cranmere Pool, &c.

With his keen eye upon hounds, and upon all the horses worth looking at, Terrell was always on the look out for amusement.

On a day, in the Dartmoor country, there was a very

large meet, of nearly 300 on horseback, to see a famous pack of hounds from another country, come on a visit to hunt for a week alternately with the native pack. There were all sorts of people on the open moor, some dressed and mounted to perfection, others turning out as best. they could, and Terrell went about to see and hear what he could get out of them, according to his wont.

There was a man of the small farmer kind, dressed for the occasion in a clean, white, working-suit of duck, and riding an active horse, bare ridged, with nothing on him but a cart bridle, blinkers and all. The horse carried nothing but the bridle and man. Before the word was given to move off and draw for a fox, there had been a

"Wishtman's Wood was not far off, and there they would begin their draw for fulmart." Wistman's Wood, 1892.

great deal of riding to and fro, to look at the hounds, say a word to friends, etc. After a while, the man's white trousers showed a stain of blood. Terrell had been watching this man, rather impressed with his appearance: he always liked small farmers, and lived amongst them. He went up to him, and said in his usual cheerful familiar manner, looking at the blood on his trousers, "Hallo! hath a galled ee?"

"Nau," said the man (the usual Devonshire for no), "I've a galled he, but 't was which he should."

Terrell looked round to me with one of his most amusing smiles on his face.

The Devonshire expression, "which he should," demands further explanation. It means, which party should get the better of another in any contest whatever, and is very much used as a short way of expressing the case. Another illustration will serve to make the use of it clearer.

I was riding with Terrell near a Dartmoor farm. We came to the gate of the farmyard, which he opened and rode in with me. There were a young couple, the wife, a nice-looking young woman, at the door of the house, and the husband, a fine young fellow, at work in the yard. Terrell "passed the time o' day to them," which means that he wished them good morning, and said a few pleasant and amusing things to them in his usual cheery way, and leaving them laughing, we went on our way.

He said to me, "Do ee know why I took ee in there?"

I said, "No. Why?"

He said, "They two were married seven year agone, and it has been 'which he should' with them till the other day, when her knacked under to un.

This young woman had been trying to hold her own, and have her own way with her husband for seven years, and at last had given it up.

"I was riding with Terrell near a Dartmoor farm. There were a young couple, the wife, a nice-looking young woman, at the door of the house, and the husband, a fine young fellow, at work in the yard." Lower Merripit farm 1889.

Terrell knew all his neighbours, and many more besides, intimately, and he thought this curious struggle was worth my attention, and the subjects worth seeing, which I thought too, and it made an impression on me, otherwise I should not have remembered it so long. They were a very nice-looking pair, anyway, and evidently on very good terms with Terrell. They had probably asked his advice, as many did, but he would not tell their secrets, nor did he tell me any particulars. I knew better than to ask him; he would have turned me off with some joke, showing plainly that he did not mean to be cross-questioned – no one could do that better than he. The "which he should" part of the business was notorious in the neighbourhood, and was no secret.

There was not much "which he should" with Terrell. He had a way with him that no one seemed inclined to dispute, and his influence over other people at times was remarkable. This was due partly to his curious command of language, coupled with the tone and manner of expressing himself, and partly to his innate cleverness, quickness of perception in seeing the strong and weak sides of a question, with a pretty good will of his own. He was quick to decide, and strong in expression, which alone go a long way.

I was much amused, on one occasion, at the effect he produced on a perfect stranger. A group of us happened to be on one side of a nasty, dangerous fence, and the stranger was the other side. Hounds were not running, and there was a gate not far off. One of us, not myself, said to Terrell:

"Make him come over, Terrell," knowing well enough he could if he chose.

Terrell said, "Get away with ee, he'll break his neck."

"Oh, no! he'll be all right," was the answer.

Terrell looked at' the fence again, and then called out, "Come on!"

He said this "Come on" in such an indescribably emphatic and take-no-denial manner, that the stranger immediately responded by riding over and joining us.

He always knew his men. At another time, we were riding from covert to covert, hounds not running, along a lane; and a young fellow, who had mistaken his way, found himself on the wrong side of a very bad fence, with a dangerous drop into the lane. He rode his horse at the fence again and again, but the horse refused. When we were tired of waiting, we moved on, and one of us said to Terrell:

"Tell him the way out."

Terrell said, "He'll come over, I *know* the man."

And he did come over.

A very ludicrous scene took place one fine day in spring, when we had run a fox a ring over a stiff country, and the hounds having run their fox to earth we were all assembled in a field outside a covert.

Terrell had bought a horse for an old friend, who was by way of being a sportsman, but did not know much about it. This friend was present on a chestnut mare. Terrell caught sight of him, and said:

"Where's your horse?"

"I've sold him," said the friend.

"What! sold the horse I bought for ee?"

"No," said the friend, "I'm riding him."

"God bless the man!" said Terrell. "That's a mare you're riding of, where's your horse?"

The friend looked down, and said, " I thought it wasn't my saddle."

"Your zaddle!" said Terrell. "Why, it isn't your horse!"

By this time, Terrell's voice being always emphatic, and some fun usually accompanying it, all the field had gathered round.

Looking about with his hawk's eye, Terrell said,

"There's your horse," pointing to a chestnut horse, which a young fellow had been wildly riding at all the fences he could find in his way.

The friend got off the chestnut mare, went up to the horse, and said, "That's my horse."

"Is it?" said the young fellow. "I am sure I don't know."

"Yes, it's my horse," said the friend, "and see how you've been spurring him!"

"Spurring him!" said Terrell. "I should think a has. He's a been riding your horse as hard as he can go over every fence he could come to, and you've a kept a fresh horse for he."

The friend was a very careful, steady rider, afraid of hurting his horse, or possibly himself; by riding over fences.

The explanation of the affair was, that the young fellow, an officer in a regiment and a stranger, had hired a chestnut hunter for the day, which was sent on by railway to the meet. The friend had sent his horse on by the same train, in charge of the same man. The young fellow, eager for the chase, on getting out of the train, saw the man with a chestnut, jumped on the horse and rode off. The friend very deliberately came after, saw the man with the other chestnut – a mare – got on her, and never found out that he was not riding his own horse till Terrell asked him where his horse was. Terrell probably knew the horse the young fellow was riding, and when the run was over, looked out for the owner.

I never saw men laugh so much. Some got off their horses and rolled on the grass with laughing. Everything that Terrell said, his tone of voice, loud enough for everyone to hear, his manner, and his laugh, made the whole thing supremely ludicrous.

A great friend of Terrell's asked him to go with him to Cheltenham, and have some hunting there. The friend mounted Terrell on his best horse, a horse that Terrell knew very well, remarkable for his endurance. There was a very large field out, and the hounds were running. They came to a haw-haw fence, hounds were not going very fast, and Terrell did not like the look of it. He used to say that if a horse dropped his hind legs in a ditch it was going over, he might break his back. I have seen a horse die of such an accident. Terrell, seeing there was no call for hurry pulled up, and followed the ruck of the field over a pass. One of the field, who it may be supposed, had had Terrell pointed out to him as a well known sportsman from the West, in passing Terrell, and taking the haw-haw, turned round in his saddle, and said to Terrell, in a jeering tone, "Ah! ah!" He was a person in authority, and it was not very civil, but Terrell's reputation had probably excited his jealousy. Terrell, of course, took no notice of the insult; what this personage thought was nothing to him, he had to take care of his friend's favourite horse.

The run proved a good one, and a trial to horses. They came to a piece of plough, going up hill. This personage's horse found it too much for him, and Terrell, with his stout horse full of go under his careful riding, passed this gentleman with ease in a good, strong, hunting gallop. Terrell knew how to ride up hill, or down hill, either, as well as any man. Seeing the other horse giving up, and getting out of the run altogether, Terrell turned round in his saddle and said, "Ah! ah!" The great man was so offended that he never spoke to Terrell again. So much for great men in Terrell's eyes!

He went with me and his daughter stag-hunting in the North of Devon. A Tayvistock young man joined us at the covert-side on Exmoor, and remarked that he did not see the sport of stag-hunting – there were no fences for men to ride at, get falls, and that sort of fun.

Terrell said, "'T's according to whether you go to see the shass, or men valling off."

He knew Hicks, of Bodmin, as a matter of course, and called him the merriest man in the West. I asked Terrell to meet Hicks at dinner, and there were others with them. Somebody said something at the beginning of the dinner, it was neither Hicks nor Terrell, which set the table in a roar, and there was nothing but roars of laughter afterwards. Both Hicks and Terrell were at their best. Terrell said to me the next morning, "Twas such a ridic'lous dinner, you couldn't ate nor drink."

He was staying at a very large, good house, where there was a party of ladies and gentlemen also staying. The housekeeper happened to be a distant relation of his, and he went from the drawing-room to the housekeeper's room, in his own natural way, amusing the company in both by his pleasant talk. His host, a gentleman of the first water, admired his manner of doing it, and was much struck with the utter absence of any commonplace vulgarity in him.

He had many good maxims concerning horses, which would be well worth remembering.

He was riding a mare out hunting, and I observed how tough she seemed to be, not being a striking looking animal in any way.

I said to him, "That seems to be a good mare, Harry!"

He said, "Oh, she can't go fast enough to beat herself!"

There is more in that than appears at first sight.

A noble lord went to see Terrell with some friends, to consult him about some sporting matters, and he, of course, put some beer and cider before them. Terrell thought the peer did not do justice to his beer, and said:

"Want ee drink your beer, my little feller?"

The lord was a light weight, and saw no objection to the "little feller" part of the business; the "telling" was racy in many respects.

A friend in very early days told Terrell he could not hit a haystack with his gun.

"I'd give ee a shot at me, any day."

The friend was on horseback, and rode off. At a certain distance he lifted up his coat-tails in mockery. Terrell fired and peppered his friend considerably, drawing blood. The friend rode back in a fury, and used strong language under the sting of the shots.

Terrell said, "If you say any more of your damned nonsense, I'll give ee the other barrel."

They parted friends after all. Terrell could talk over most people. He was very young then.

Terrell used to say he knew a man at Totnes who hunted a trencher pack, and when he called off in the evening he put down a stick, and laid the hounds on at the same place the next morning.

This might have happened with deer, or with hares, if they were very scarce, and the hounds line-hunting harriers. It is an old story, but Terrell may have known a case in which a simple old huntsman hunting a trencher pack for the pot was the hero.

Terrell settled in the Dartmoor country, and hunted regularly with the Dartmoor pack. The pack originated with Mr., or Major, Pode, of Slade, who had a very famous huntsman called Johnny Roberts, and hunted fox, hare, deer, otter, or fulmart, as the case might be. Mr. Pode was succeeded by Mr. Bulteel, of Flete, who hunted fox only, and introduced much fresh blood in the pack, and whose huntsman was one Limpity, a nickname given him when a boy by Mr. Bulteel, for his peculiar walk. He was considered a great huntsman also, though his fearless and reckless riding, and his real keenness for sport, were probably his only merits.

Mr. Bulteel was succeeded by Mr. Charles Trelawny, who hunted the country with the hounds given him by

"The pack originated with Major Pode of Slade." Slade House, Cornwood, 1894.

Lady Elizabeth Bulteel, asking for no subscription for many years, in Terrell's time.

Henry Terrell, which was his real name, had farmed Ottery in the Tavistock country. But when he settled in the Dartmoor country he bought a very pretty moorland property in the parish of Sheepstor, where he spent the best part of his life. He was tempted afterwards by a heavy price to sell this place to the trustees of the Rajah of Sarawak, Sir James Brooke, but I think he never recovered leaving it, and did not settle down afterwards, till ill-health finally induced him to live with his daughter in London, where he died.

Mr. Charles Trelawny had a great idea of pace with hounds, and overdid it in that direction, as Dartmoor itself is a fast country. It was, therefore, only very well-bred horses of the stoutest families, in first rate condition, that could live with hounds all over Dartmoor, especially in a good run where steep hills were the chief obstacles to pace. It is necessary to be quick as well as to be able to go a good pace on Dartmoor, for hounds can slip away, down a deep combe for instance, and disappear as if by magic, unseen and unheard.

Terrell on one occasion was riding pretty close to hounds, on a sort of day when they might get away at a great pace, as he knew well enough, though he was the last man in the world to ride over hounds. He always knew what to do. At the end of the run he was first up as usual, and the master was rather annoyed at not being so well placed, himself.

He said, in a tone of reproach, "If gentlemen will ride so close to hounds, how can they run their fox?"

Which was a reproof intended for Terrell, as all the field knew. But the hounds had happened to run their fox remarkably well.

Terrell said, in an equally loud tone of voice, "They that be behind always vind vault with they that be bevore."

Rather a knock-down answer.

Some of the old hunting-men were perpetually referring to "Johnny Roberts's day," with lamentations for a time of perfect happy hunting, past and gone, never to be seen again.

It was the old style, animals scarce and wild, hounds slower than they are now, with good nose and plenty of tongue, and horses slower. There was no doubt about Johnny Roberts's riding at all, events.

There is a ludicrous account, with a clever sketch, of a great run after a fox, when Johnny Roberts rode his horse to a standstill, no one else up; he took a promising looking horse out of a plough – no ploughman would think of refusing Johnny Roberts anything – and finished the run on him, bareridged, the only one at the death. I am inclined deeply to respect Johnny Roberts's memory, for no man could have left behind him such an overpowering reputation, unless there were something in him.

Harry Terrell's ideas were fresh and new, many of them

his own, but he always knew what was going on in the sporting world. His opinions therefore sometimes differed from those that prevailed in "Johnny Roberts's day," and the old hunting-men would reprove him for setting on foot novel notions, not sanctioned by the great Prophet.

A very large old fox had been driven to earth in a great covert, and it was decided to take him out, which was a formidable undertaking. Terrell's beautiful little white rough terrier was "in," and they had to dig to her. As she never ceased fighting the fox, and "telling" about it, they could dig to her "noising." A dispute arose, as a matter of course, as to what ought to be done, and Terrell, as usual, gave a very decided opinion; on which a well known old hunting-man said,

"Ah! it wouldn't have been like that in Johnny Roberts's day."

Terrell said, "I was sartain Johnny Roberts would be drawed in my teeth. Johnny Roberts was a good sportsman, I've no doubt, but he had a forgitful lot of disciples."

They dug down to the little bitch in the end, and took out the fox. A bigger mask, with old broken teeth, I never saw.

Cock-fighting was the fashion in Terrell's earlier days, and he always had good gamecocks with hens to match, long after it had been given up by the law-abiders.

There used to be cock-pits in many places, some in a room set apart in gentlemen's houses. According to the original Act of Parliament, it was held, that if cocks were fought elsewhere than in a cock-pit, that is anywhere which had never been used before as a cock-pit, the prosecution failed. This was either over-ruled, or an Act of Parliament passed to meet the point.

Meanwhile, cocks were fought on Dartmoor, and Terrell had usually something to do with it. Having been brought up in such a sporting place as Tavistock, he knew all about it, and could "heel" a cock as well as any man. To heel a cock is to put on the steel spurs, which is a delicate operation, for if they are not put on exactly at the right angle in relation to the leg, the cock may kill himself instead of his enemy. Cock-spurs were made of steel, with great care, or sometimes of silver, or, as steel must have been the best metal for the purpose, of steel silvered over. They were kept in leather cases lined with velvet, as jewelled brooches are now. They were humane contrivances in one sense, because they inflicted fatal stabs, where the natural spur would only wound and make the battle a very prolonged affair.

There was an old sporting squire, a friend of Terrell's, of whom many good stories were told; also of his servant, who never left him, and was a first-rate man to hounds, or at any other sport.

This servant was in constant attendance on his master, taking care of him, and looking after him, which he had done from his boyhood. In a run with the hounds, however, he would ride away from the old gentleman on his best horses, much to his master's pride and satisfaction, who well knew he could not ride the horses in the same style himself. The evening would be spent, the squire being a bachelor, in talking of the run, and how the horses had gone.

This servant was riding a horse, with a boot on his fore leg, out hunting one day. I said to him,

"Do you find that boot do any good?"

"Not a bit," he said. "God Almighty made the leg, and man" (with a broad accent on the 'a' with much emphasis) "made the bute; that's the way I looks at it.

The squire was old, and slowly going out of the world, when Terrell said to me,

"Let's go and cheer un up a bit."

He made an appointment with me, and one morning

soon after I called for him at Burrator; he had his pony ready, and he threw a sack across the pony's back behind the saddle, on one side of which were two game cocks, and on the other side one to balance. Two of them were young birds. We rode over the moor that we might not meet anyone, and found our way to the squire's mansion. It was on that occasion Terrell showed me his cock-spurs in an old case, lined with velvet, which had evidently once been turned out of hand in very tasteful style.

We met the squire and his faithful servant, who were also ready with game cocks. The "heeling" process then took place, and I saw with what care the heeling had to be done. Terrell and the squire's sporting servant, who was a clever and, at the same time, a curious man, seemed to be equally skilled in the art, and talked of it in very technical language.

Three game cocks were produced to match Terrell's, and the battles, one after another, were fought in the farmyard. Notwithstanding that the squire's game cocks, of which he was very proud, were on their own dunghill, or near it, the end of the battles was that Terrell's three cocks killed all three of the squire's. One of the squire's was a fine, beautiful bird, which had been given to him by an old cock-fighting friend, for its great merits. Terrell's birds, after their journey over the moor in a bag on a pony, did not look particularly flourishing, either in plumage, colour, or condition, but they went into battle with a will, and, for some reason, which appeared to me inexplicable, they killed all three of their opponents. All the cocks fought with fury as soon as they were put down, not hesitating an instant.

This did not prove a very successful mode of cheering up the old squire in his last days. He came to the fight at first with the greatest interest, and looked on Terrell's birds as if they had come to their doom, but as his cocks were killed one after another he looked very serious, and when the last and favourite one fell, he turned on his heel to walk to his house, saying it was "a barbarous practice," though one that he had pursued all his life.

"Yes, yes," said Terrell, "that's all very well for an old cockfighter to say, but he'd a sung a different song if his cocks had a killed mine.

"Here," he said to the servant, whom he had known all the man's life, "You take my cocks and comfort un with 'em. I don't want 'em."

One of them was quite a young bird, and I suppose his winning his battle was a mere accident, which, with the long steel spurs, must have been a common result. The spur seemed to strike the enemy almost with as straight a point as a small sword would in the hands of an expert swordsman, and, doubtless, the angle at which it is placed on the leg of the cock has much to do with this direct and effective stab. Possibly Terrell's cocks had been better "heeled" than the squire's.

This same servant of the squire's, on the occasion of a gentleman settling in the neighbourhood, who was not a hunting man, undertook, on his own account, to see the stranger, and "persuade un," as he said, not to kill foxes. The interview ended in the servant offering to fight the newcomer. What passed between them no one knew, but the stranger was certainly a gentleman, and proved to be a pleasant neighbour. The squire's servant must have gone on his self-imposed errand in a very hot, fox-hunting frame of mind, and not being known as a great man, or the shadow of a great man, had not been received in the spirit he expected.

Harry Terrell greatly enjoyed the humour of the relations between this squire and his confidential servant, who had been born on the estate, and had been a sort of attendant from childhood, ending in the squire being unable to do anything at all without him. They were both of Dartmoor, isolated, self-reliant (as a couple), and eccentric. The servant, at all events, was a thorough sportsman, good at all sports, and the squire thought of nothing else but sport, though given to reading, and writing too.

I agreed to meet Terrell at a certain bridge, to ride sixteen miles with him, to meet the otter hounds in the summer. A lady had asked us to take her boy with us, a schoolboy about fourteen years old, who arrived at the bridge a little late. It was very early in the morning. Terrell greeted him with,

"Well, young six-foot, has your mother sent any plaster with ee?"

The boy did not seem to understand the allusion so early in the day, the full appreciation of it might come later on.

When he had ridden on soberly about ten miles, the boy said,

"Is it far from here, Mr. Terrell ?" Terrell said, "Oh! you 'm like that, be ee?" and that was all the answer he got. Terrell was talking about sport to me, but he was always kind to boys, and liked entering them, as he called it.

We had our day's sport on the river, and left to ride home our sixteen miles about four o'clock in the afternoon.

Terrell went to a very large house near, and rang the bell at the front door. I did not know what he was about He knew the people a little, but not well. A butler dressed to receive company, answered the bell. Terrell said,

"Here – give this young gentleman something to ate, will ee?"

The butler was very polite, took the boy inside, and Terrell and I adjourned to the stables with the horses to wait.

I said to Terrell, "Why did you do that? Do you know them well enough?"

His answer was, "Do you think that there boy could ride home with us without anything to ate? Why, he'd a fainted."

We waited about half-an-hour for the boy, when he came out refreshed, and said the butler had taken him into the dining-room, and given him to eat and to drink of the best.

It was very characteristic of Terrell. His manner, as usual, had been all-sufficient to get what he wanted. The butler was a gentleman in behaviour, as all good butlers are, but the boy was a perfect stranger. Terrell required nothing for himself, and asked for nothing, but the boy was in his charge, and he must return him to his mother safe and sound. It was a hard day for a young fellow on a pony.

I met Terrell in the street of a town, and asked him, as usual, "How is Mrs. Terrell?"

He said, "Margaret is not very well. She has been up all night with one of the maids that was bad."

"Oh!" I said, "I am sorry for that. What was the matter with the maid?"

"A vlea" (flea) "kicked her, I reckon," said Terrell

This expression is a common term of contempt in Devonshire for a slight ailment made much of in the mind of the afflicted subject. I remember in my early nursery days, if I complained of being unwell, as children sometimes do, the nursery maids would say, "What! has a vlea kicked ee, my dear?" It is rather expressive.

"Object" is a word often used in Devonshire for an evil appearance. If anyone is much disfigured it would be said he was an object, or if a child has covered itself with mud it is said, "What a objic you've a made of yourzelf!"

There had been a new farm house built in a lovely valley in Sheepstor, which, being outwardly four walls

"There had been a new farmhouse built in a lovely valley." Sheepstor, a painting by John White Abbot

(by kind permission of Christies Images Ltd)

only, and whitewashed, Terrell expected would spoil the picturesque of the valley. He was talking to a farmer's wife on the opposite hill, and said, pointing to the new house,

"That isn't such a bad object, after all."

She said, "Objic, Mr. Terrell! I think 't es a very pretty houze."

He got a good deal of amusement in those little ways, and told the stories to me. He would ask a man or a woman, whom he thought were promising subjects, a question with an object, and I could see from the expression of his face the intense amusement he got from their answers. It was one of his many ways of amusing himself.

I was walking with Terrell through the streets of Plymouth, and he saw hanging out of a high window some herbs – his eyes were always everywhere. He said, "There's a feller who makes organ tay" (tea). I believe *tay* is the right pronunciation and the oldest, in French it is, of course, *thé*.

I asked for an explanation, and he told me that herbalists, so-called, collect certain plants, which they dry, and of which they make tea, said to be of very beneficial effect on the human organs, especially those of the gentler sex. Hence it has come to pass that a writer on Devonshire dialect has called the herb *pennyroyal-organ*; a great mistake, pennyroyal being only one ingredient for organ tay.

There was a very famous ancient sportsman, who kept a pack of fox-hounds, and lived hospitably in a densely wooded country.

He was a great fox hunter and whist player, and divided his time pretty fairly between the two.

Terrell was there after hunting on a Friday, and they agreed to shut up the room, play whist, and have their meals, without looking to see what time it was, until they were tired, and wanted to leave off. They were half-a-dozen, including the squire, who was a bachelor, and orders were given to his housekeeper accordingly.

When they were tired of whist the light was let into the room, and they found it was Monday morning. They had played whist continually, those who cut out of the game taking their meals and their naps. The details of the experiment were contrived by the old squire and his housekeeper. It may be said to have been a good carouse. Liquor, in the shape of punch or tea, was not spared, and they were men, old friends, who could drink without getting drunk.

This same old squire kept on his hounds until his death at a good age. He was gouty, and used to go out with his ancient huntsman and old pack of hounds more as a habit than for real sport. At last Terrell said of him, "He has only wan (one) fox in his country, and a can't find he."

There used to be a week's hunting at Ivybridge in the spring, with a stranger pack of hounds, to hunt every day for the week, an old custom that is still kept up. The Dartmoor hounds were then Mr. Trelawny's.

We left off late one day at the extreme east of Dartmoor. A member of the hunt, who lived some way beyond the western borders of the moor, said he must go home to his wife and children across the moor; it was too far to go by road. We all asked him if he knew his way. He said, with great confidence, "Oh, yes; I have been the way often," as he no doubt had, but it was getting dark.

We looked doubtful, but, he was a determined, not to say obstinate, man, and would not listen to our advice. Wishing us goodbye, he rode off on his nice black mare.

The next morning, hunting again from Ivybridge, where we were having a festive time with our guests, as

"The next morning, hunting again from Ivybridge, where we were having a festive time with our guests." A view of the Ivy Bridge, 1830.

we were drawing a brake on the borders of the moor, about half-past eleven o'clock, a ghastly appearance came over the hill.

It was our friend of the night before. He was a tall, lank man, now very pale in the face, his white leathers, top-boots, and red coat, covered with black bog earth, riding a small, rough pony. He appeared like the ghost of himself of the day before coming out of the moor.

We asked him what was the matter, but he said he was in a hurry to get home to his wife, and passed on without explaining, going by the road this time.

We soon heard all about it from a hunting friend, who had lent him the pony.

He had missed his way in the dark on the moor, and had struck a path which led to the bogs, instead of the Abbot's Way, which is a perfectly sound way through the bogs, used by the Abbots and Monks of the olden days, when those of Buckland Monachorum and Tavistock, on the western side of the moor, or Buckfastleigh, on the eastern side, used to go a-visiting.

The path our hunting friend had followed led him to the bogs, and his mare had got in. He persuaded her to struggle out of one only to get into another, and at last she gave it up. He then proceeded to a warrener, who lived on the moor near by, to get help. The warrener went some little distance for some miners, and they got the mare out by main force. It was a beautiful, calm night, and the miners' dip candles, with which they go underground, fixed in their hats with clay, burned brightly all round the bog which held the mare.

After she was safely out our friend went to the warrener's cottage, eat all his bacon and drank all his cider. He described the waking up and "chirruping" of the children, one by one, as the daylight appeared. He then led his mare to the nearest fox-hunting friend, who put her up in his stables, and lent him a rough pony to take him home. He had spent the night in the bogs, had refreshed himself until morning as well as he could at the warrener's, had led his mare to his friend's stables, jumped on the pony to ride home as soon as he could on such a beast, had neither slept, washed, shaved, or combed his hair, and came like an apparition on a large field of fox-hunters, who were in all the pride and glory of the morning, scarlet coats and white leathers, the "object" that I have described.

As he started the evening before, against the best advice, to get home to his wife and children, what they thought of the adventure was not reported.

These eccentric beings will shortly be extinct, with the polecat and peregrine falcon. The eccentricity developed by living in out-lying places, their own masters, doing and thinking whatever they pleased, without interference or censure from anyone, had the effect of producing some wonderful characters, never more to visit the scenes of earthly joys. Railways, telegraphs, and the newspaper press, have turned them all into a mass of so-called gentry, as like one another as pease. I remember the days before railways, and I remember some very eccentric characters. Harry Terrell may be said to be one of them, but there was something in him quite out of the common, and he would have been good to meet in any society.

The friend I have just told of was very eccentric, came of a very famous eccentric stock, and he performed many eccentric deeds. One is worth mentioning by way of illustration. Most of the very eccentric men were also hunting men, in the days when they went out hunting, and did not go out for a ride, as many now do.

This friend, one day out hunting, jammed his leg in a granite gateway, which did not trouble him much, but on the road home some unsportsmanlike companions stopped at a wayside inn for some gin and water which he would have scorned touching till after dinner, it was a maxim in the old days of long rides to covert and back never to stop on the road, but to take your horse home to his stables as soon as possible without going fast.

When the others asked for hot gin and water, which the barmaid brought out, he asked for some also, and the barmaid brought him the steaming glass, with a spoon in it, as usual. Her astonishment was great when she saw him take it deliberately from her, with a "Thank ee," and, instead of carrying it to his mouth, pour it carefully down the inside of his top-boot. Her face was a study. She did not know that his leg was giving him pain – he would be the last to complain – nor that he thought hot gin and water might be as comforting to the outside of his leg as it was to the inside of other people. He paid his sixpence, and went on with the others, as if he had done nothing at all unusual. It would not have been like him to offer an explanation of what he chose to do to anyone, and the barmaid probably thought he was a madman.

This same friend held theories, and was prone to argue a monstrous heterodox view of some simple custom in hunting, farming, or anything else, the whole way to covert, some ten to seventeen miles, and the whole way back again. About six of us – Harry Terrell one – used to go on to the meets across Dartmoor together, and after all his opinions never turned a hair.

There was an old fox-hunter, a great authority with the Dartmoor, and had been a good man in his day, who was always engaged in a wordy war with Terrell about sporting and everything else, carried on with very good temper, more, perhaps, for the fun of Terrell's talk than for anything else.

When this old gentleman laid down the law, which he was apt to do, Terrell would tell him he was "past," and could not see a hound either in covert or in chase, which was true enough.

We were drawing a young plantation on the borders of the moor, with undergrowth of furze as thick as a mat.

Terrell said, "Give 'em time, 't is very thick."

The old gentleman as usual contradicted him, and said, "Not a bit of it. Do you call that thick?"

Terrell said, "I'll bet ee ten shillings you wan't get through un in twenty minutes."

The covert was not more than two or three acres.

"Done," said the old gentleman.

I held the stakes, and the old gentleman got off his horse, which Terrell held, and proceeded in breeches and boots to struggle through the covert, and I held my watch to note the time.

It was so thick the old gentleman could scarcely get through, but he had plenty of pluck, and by working very hard, he appeared at the opposite side in nineteen minutes. I thought at his age he never would have got out of that gorse at all.

The rest of the field had gone on, and I remained

with Terrell, watch and stakes in hand. When I handed over the money, the old gentleman said, "Stop, I can't get on my horse yet."

Terrell's laugh was worth hearing. It was blowing a cold cutting wind from the east on an exposed bit of moor, and the old gentleman had to completely strip his lower limbs and bare them to the blast to pick out the prickles from his breeches, whilst Terrell held his horse, congratulating him on his having won his bet, and saying he would not go through it, himself, for ten shillings on any account.

He seemed to think the ten shillings well laid out.

It was at least ten minutes before the old gentleman could mount his horse, and he was in misery the rest of the day, not relieved by Terrell's ridicule.

It turned out a memorable day recorded in the annals of the hunt.

Just as we came up to the covert which the hounds were drawing, we saw a fine old fox go away over Dartmoor. The hounds went a tremendous pace, and most of the field were soon left far behind. Some of the first flight rode well up, until the hounds went over the bogs, where it was impossible to go fast, and they had then to ride to points.

Terrell, who on that day was riding one of his famous ponies by "Jack-in-the-Green," soon saw that at such a pace no fox could stay long before hounds, and turning his pony's head rode straight for well-known earths about five miles off, which we used to call the dungeon, where he knew the fox must go if he saved his life. He was the only one of a large field who saw the hounds, close to their fox, run him to earth there.

As I saw what Terrell was doing, I left the hounds to follow him, and was up just in time to see the pack stop at the dungeon. On the hills all round were soon seen men in scarlet, and otherwise, looking for the hounds, which had disappeared in the bogs at a pace very seldom seen even on Dartmoor, where they always go fast.

"Look at um," said Terrell. "They don't know where they be!"

It was impossible in this run to ride to hounds, because the pace over the bogs was so fast. The hounds ran a half-circle, and Terrell rode what he called the string of the bow. He knew the ground so well, that when he saw the line taken by the fox, he was sure the dungeon could be his only point, though it was so far off. Terrell also saw the fox, and judged he was good enough to reach it, which he only just did. It was one of the fastest runs on record.

There was a well-known sporting parson in the hunt, who was a most enthusiastic otter hunter, among other sports. He was getting into the vale of years, and, as he had known the great Johnny Roberts in early days, he was for ever quoting him as a superior authority to any mere modern, which excited Terrell's ire.

Out otter-hunting we were all collected in a road, coffee-housing, as it is called, while hounds were drawing a stream in a deep valley below, on a cold, raw day, with no scent, and not a prospect of a find.

The parson was laying down the law according to Johnny Roberts.

Terrell said to us, "I'll make he go to water."

He went up to the parson, and said casually, "How old be ee?"

"Sixty-four," said the parson.

"Not you b'ant," said Terrell. As it was in his customary tone it gave no offence. "You baint more than sixty."

"I tell you I'm sixty-four," was the answer.

"Well," said Terrell, "whatever you be, I thought you was a good entry once, but you've a knacked it sooner than anybody I knaw."

"What do you mean, Terrell ?"

"Mane! Why, here you be on your horse, about in the road, and the hounds be drawing there under ee. I knaw the time when you'd a been up to neck in water with urn. Look at urn down there."

Terrell never "went to water" himself in those days, unless it was on horseback.

The effect was ludicrous. The sporting parson got off his horse, and rushed impetuously down a steep copse into the river, cheering the hounds, though there was not an atom of scent.

An old friend, who was in the meadow below, called out in astonishment, "What are you about? There's no scent, and you'll catch your death-a-cold* in this weather."

"It is that feller Terrell," was the naive reply.

If anything happened in his neighbourhood requiring advice or assistance Terrell was always sent for. He was once sent for to a small farmer, who had hung himself in despair at the loss of five sheep, which he could not find. The hanging had not been done effectually, and Terrell cut the man down, and helped to restore him. The poor fellow could not well afford the loss of five sheep, and it had preyed on his mind.

Two years afterwards, when hounds were drawing on the opposite side of the moor, in a wild quarter, Terrell saw these same five sheep making away from the hounds as fast as they could go up a steep hill. He knew them directly, and, when he went home, told the man where to find them, who went to fetch them, and was comforted. They had lived all that time a perfectly wild life many miles from their farm. Terrell had a wonderful eye for cattle and everything else. He knew his neighbour's sheep directly he saw them. Hounds on the moor must be very steady, and the Dartmoor pack are remarkably so. A sheep will jump up before them, and

---

* A common expression.

go away like a deer, but they take no notice of either sheep or hare.

Terrell was at Billingsgate, and saw a fish he did not know. He went up to the stall and said, "What sort of fish do ee call that? I never saw one like it before."

The woman said, "No. There's clotted cream where you come from."

He laughed when he told me the story.

An old fox-hunting friend, Sir Lewis Western, who held curious opinions of his own, a sort of country gentleman much more common fifty years ago in the outlying districts than he is now, a gentleman in every respect, manly and humane, talking with a Devonshire accent, once gave Terrell a terrier.

Terrell complained that this particular terrier was eager to go to ground if there was no fox there, but if there was a fox in the earth or hole nothing would induce him to go near it.

Sir Lewis said, "What can ee want more? If he won't go in, you know he's there, and you can dig for 'n."

Harry Terrell was not a rich man. He had an income which he made enough, and never was in debt. He had a good house, and very pretty small property, with some coverts of his own, on the borders of Dartmoor, in the parish of Sheepstor – Burrator – and he spent most of his time on Dartmoor, either hunting or shooting, with a hunter and pony, and a setter or two. He knew the whole of Dartmoor thoroughly.

His knowledge of people was extensive. It was not a mere acquaintance, but might be expressed by his own way of saying, "I know un," which meant a good deal. He knew everyone within his reach, but he was not a wanderer far out of the west of Devon.

In early days, before dealers scoured the country, and

picked up every three-year-old worth looking at, his keen knowledge of a horse, and of pedigrees, with his fine memory of all the deeds of a horse and his ancestors, led him to buy young ones of promise off a farm, break them to hunting until they had a name, which they were sure to get with him on their back, and sell them at good prices, when six, seven, or eight years old as the case might be. But in course of time he was disgusted with "dayling," as he called dealing, the dealers by profession competing with him. One of his maxims was, to see as many horses as possible to get your eye in.

He much resented any attempt to "do" him, the art of deception so notoriously common with horse dealers, as the following story will show.

He was not easily "done," but his intimate friend, Squire Tallyo, as he has been called, succeeded in selling him a horse which was not quite the thing.

"I'll mind ee out, I warn ee," he said. Two very common Devonshire expressions for "serving out," and "warrant."

Tallyo ought to have been warned, for he knew Terrell well, but he fell a victim.

Terrell allowed many months to pass, behaving as if the whole, affair had been forgotten. When it had been practically forgotten, he appeared at a great meet of the foxhounds on Dartmoor, on a very nice looking horse. He seemed rather to avoid his friend, as he was wont to do sometimes when he wished his horse to be out of the crowd, especially a new one, and he rode over a fence or two as if to try him. Tallyo, who had an eye for a horse, watched him, and at last went up to him, and asked him what horse he was on.

Terrell was mysterious, and said, "Never you mind. What's that to you? B'ant I to ride a good horse as well as anybody else?" and he rode away.

This excited Tallyo's curiosity, who watched him and his horse with still greater attention.

The horse looked remarkably well, and Harry Terrell rode him to perfection. He still avoided Tallyo, as if he were taking particular care of his horse.

At last Tallyo's curiosity overcame him, and he rode up to Terrell to ask whether the horse was for sale.

"No. You shan't have un; I'll have as fine a horse as you," said Terrell, and rode away again.

Tallyo thought this was very unusual behaviour, and supposed Terrell had got hold of something of which he intended to make a high price. He made up his mind to have the horse, totally forgetting all about the former transaction.

He at last went up to Terrell and said, "I will give you both my horses (he had two out) and five pounds besides, for that horse."

It should be remembered that Harry Terrell was famous for having good horses. He never rode a bad one; if he got hold of one, which must have been very rarely, no one ever heard of the animal.

Terrell then said, "Well, you always have your own way. Have ee got the five pounds about ee?"

"Yes," said Tallyo; "here it is."

They then changed horses and saddles. The transaction took place before many of the field, sport not being great, and Terrell sent the second horse to Burrator.

When that horse had disappeared, Terrell turned quietly round in his saddle and said,

"Now, my pretty little pictur, I've a done ee. I wouldn't give this horse, without the other, for half-a-dozen of they you're on.

"Pictur" (picture) is a favourite and endearing expression in Devonshire; nursery maids, especially, say to a baby, "Oh, my pretty pictur!"

Tallyo could not make it out at all. He found the horse charming, and, as the day was over, he rode him home, reflecting what could be amiss. The next morning he had him out to look at him, and could see nothing wrong. He had him saddled, and rode him at a Devonshire bank, such as he had seen him take quite well with Terrell. The horse breasted the bank, and did not rise at it. He tried him again, and came to the conclusion that, good hack as he was, he was blind. He sent for a dealer at once to get rid of the annoyance. As soon as the dealer saw him he said, "I know that horse very well; it is a peculiar case; he is as blind as a bat, and his eyes don't show it."

But," said Tallyo, "he'll jump."

"Oh, yes," said the dealer; "over banks of a certain height, if you jerk his reins at the right time.

The mystery was explained, and the dealer had the horse at his own price.

This very old friend, who had had many a frolic with Harry Terrell, was so enraged at this "serving out" affair, that he cut Harry Terrell, and would not speak to him, but he got the worst of it at that game also.

They had to meet at the covert side any day of the week. Tallyo, a country gentleman, a good dresser, in his scarlet, got up in neat perfection. Harry Terrell, in his black coat – he never wore scarlet – breeches, and topboots, looking the thorough sportsman, of great authority, which he was.

He could make anyone laugh by his own peculiar way of saying things. When he found Tallyo cut him, he said to anyone near him, loud enough to be heard some way off, "Do ee see that man over there in a red coat? He wont spake to me because I've a done un."

He got the laugh on his side in this way, laughing himself to make the whole affair as ridiculous as possible, till at last Tallyo could stand it no longer, and rode up to him, and said,

"Harry, for God's sake shake hands; what's the good of going on about it?"

The pretty quarrel was over.

Terrell was out hunting one day on foot, when a friend,

a good staunch friend by-the-bye, whom he knew very well, said to him, "Where's your horse?"

"I haven't got one sound enough," said Terrell; "and I haven't anything to ride."

"You can have one of my steers," his friend said. "I don't see why they shouldn't do as well as a horse."

Terrell called for this squire at his mansion one day, on his way to covert to ride on with him. He got off his horse, and was just going into the house, when he met the squire, who said to him,

"Where be ee going?"

"Oh! just to say good-morning to the misess"(mistress).

"Come on, come on. She'll tell ee to death," said the squire.

The "misess" was a great talker, and so was Terrell.

There are one or two touching stories of this old friend of Terrell, a much older man than he was, which Terrell told me of him, and will not be out of place, because it was part of Terrell's character to feel their pathos.

The hounds had driven a fox into a drain on some land, the owner of which was a friend of this squire, but at the same time an enemy of foxes and of hunting. The fox having been driven into the drain, the owner objected to have his well-constructed drains disturbed, and, as he was an enemy to foxes, the men stopped the fox in, and left him, it might be supposed, to starve.

The next morning, before the owner had risen from breakfast, the squire appeared at his door, having ridden about eight miles before breakfast.

He said, "Harry" (another Harry), "I can't sleep by night thinking of that fox. Do ee let us take him out and kill him."

This Harry was so touched that he said, "I will have the drain opened at once, and he shall go free; not a hair of him shall be hurt."

This squire was very upright and downright in all his ways, was supposed not to be sensitive; he took care to conceal it if he was, and he scorned all anxiety. His sons were brought up to do much as they pleased, and understood that there would be no anxiety about them whatever they did, and they must take care of themselves. If out hunting, especially, nobody was to wait for them.

In his old age he became more sensitive, but would not show it.

His youngest son went out hunting, and did not come home. It was the way of the house for no one to wait dinner, and in due time everyone went to bed. The old squire, however, could not sleep, and was anxious. He knew that if no accident had befallen his son he would be sleeping at the house of a certain friend. He got up quietly in the dead of night, went to the stable and saddled his horse, rode about seven miles to the friend's house, looked into the stable window, where he saw his son's mare comfortably at rest in her stall, and he rode home to bed again, satisfied and contented.

He hoped no one would find out this weakness of his, as he would have called it, but a man of note, so well known by every soul, could hardly ride seven miles and back, even at night, without being observed by someone. Besides, his grooms must have known his horse had been out, but no one dared ask why. However, the facts were known to a few – Terrell for one.

This same squire lost his eldest son. The day of the funeral he appeared out hunting, the melancholy business having been got through early. Someone, who ought to have known better, but there are always fools about, said to him, "I did not expect to see you out, squire." He said, "I can't bide home; I can't bide home." Game is scarce on Dartmoor. There are snipe, blackcock, some few wild hares and partridges, a few wild duck, and occasionally almost any sort of bird. Terrell gave me a quail and a stormy petrel, both of which he had shot on Dartmoor. I was sitting next him at a dinner given by a hospitable person in a large country house to a large party, all men, and mostly sporting men. I always got near him if I could, to hear what he would say. I heard his next neighbour, who was a stranger, ask him about Dartmoor, to whom he gave his usual graphic replies.

The stranger asked him, "Is there any game on Dartmoor?"

"Yes, sure," said Terrell.

"What sort?"

"All sorts. Snipe, hare, woodcock, black game, duck."

"Is there much black game on Dartmoor?"

"About wan (one) every eighty miles." The stranger stared at him, but ended by being amused.

On thinking over this answer, I came to the conclusion that it was as strictly correct as it well could be.

If, taking the year through, as Terrell did, you went in search of black game on Dartmoor, you might kill one for every eighty miles you went, though at times you might come upon a few together, and bag half-a-dozen in a day.

Chapter Six

THE RAJAH BROOKE AND BURRATOR

Burrator is on the western borders of Dartmoor, and also on the western borders of the small moorland parish of Sheepstor. There is a Tor on Burrator, of course, a high granite rock overlooking a steep, dense copse, which forms the eastern bank of the river Mewe, or Meavy, a bright clear stream falling over granite boulders, and noising, as we say in Devonshire, as it goes.

This river is the boundary of the parishes of Sheepstor and Meavy, and is famous as the source from which Drake took the water, by a long leat or watercourse, to supply Plymouth and the shipping there. The purity of the water and the beauty of the stream is striking. It flows rapidly under Burrator, the fall being great, and foams over the granite bed of rocks. The bank opposite to Burrator is also a piece of dense copse and waste, in the parish of Meavy. Burrator Wood is a good fox covert, and when Terrell was there foxes were safe from all their enemies, except the legitimate foxhound.

Another moorland stream of sparkling purity flows close to the house of Burrator, and, tumbling over a steep bit of granite to join the Mewe, forms an exceedingly pretty waterfall of considerable height amongst the leafy copse. When a flood comes from Dartmoor these two streams, with the waterfall, make Burrator resound with their roar.

The rest of Burrator was, in Terrell's time, grass pasture. He would not plough, and farmed on what he and his fellow farmers called the green side. To be

"Burrator Wood was a good fox covert, and when Terrell was there foxes were safe from all their enemies, except the legitimate foxhound." A view of Leather Tor and the Meavy valley, by John White Abbot, 1800 (by kind permission of Christies Images Ltd).

"always on the green" was his way of expressing a cheerful countenance on all occasions, much approved of by him.

Two sides of Burrator are therefore bounded by river, and the third side, for it is a sort of triangle, by other property in the parish. It is a romantic little parish, and the land is good for the dairy.

Terrell was very hospitable by nature, though his income was small, and if anyone came to his house the guest was sure to have of the best. Mrs. Terrell was great at housekeeping, and all the pies, puddings, hams, bacon, poultry, etc., provided simple fare of the very first quality. Her recipe book, if she had one otherwise than in her head, which is doubtful, would be an invaluable treasure.

Terrell had always the best cider and beer, and a very good bottle of port wine for a friend. All Devonshire folk like cider, the most wholesome of drinks, and all Devonshire farmers used to make it, but, unhappily, leases being short, that is, seven to fourteen years, and apple trees taking twenty-five years to come to good bearing, orchards are gradually diminishing, instead of increasing, as in these fruit growing days they ought to do. In some favoured districts cider of a very fine quality is made, and Terrell used to exercise his very fine judgment in all things in buying enough for his own use. One good year in seven is said to return a very satisfactory average profit with orchards. Terrell had not an orchard at Burrator, nor of course a cider press or pound, which used to be a common appurtenance to all farms, made of good wholesome granite.

He once bought some cider of a friend, a hunting man of some celebrity and eccentricity. He complained to the friend that the cider that was sent him was vinegar, and the reply he got was, "Where can ee buy vinegar for a guinea a hogshead? " – the price usually paid for cider. Some folks like cider rather rash, as they call it, which means when it is on its way to vinegar.

His Highness, Sir James Brooks, K.C.B., Rajah of Sarawak, had been seized with sudden illness, and was ordered to Torquay by the doctors. The doctors there recommended him Dartmoor air, which is about the best to be had anywhere. The Lady Burdett-Coutts was a great friend of the Rajah, and at that time had a house at Torquay. The Rajah, while inquiring for a place on Dartmoor, went to Totnes to see a well-known land-agent. This man was one of Terrell's numerous friends, who were scattered far and wide.

As the Rajah was talking to the land-agent, Terrell happened to ride by. It occurred to him that Terrell, not being a rich man, might consent to sell Burrator at a good price, and he said to the Rajah, "That man's property would suit you exactly, and he may sell it."

The Rajah said, "I see by his face it will suit me, I never saw a healthier looking man." The land-agent called out to Terrell, saying, "Come here, I want ee."

Terrell rode up to them, and the landagent said, "Will you sell your place?"

"No," said Terrell, "I won't." Then he stopped short, and looking at the Rajah, added, "not unless I be bought out," meaning that he did not wish to sell his home, but that he was too poor a man to be justified in refusing a fancy price.

The Rajah went to see Burrator, and determined to have it. He had come to England for the purpose of promoting a trade with Sarawak, and when he was taken suddenly ill a fund was raised, to which Lady Burdett-Coutts was a large contributor, and placed in the hands of trustees, to secure the Rajah in his position of sovereign of Sarawak, both for his own sake, and for the sake of the trade to be established by him. It need not be said here that the Rajah was a very remarkable man. He had known many peoples in India and eastern lands of all sorts, and he seemed to take in Terrell at a glance.

Terrell had heard about the Rajah, and being a first-rate judge of mankind, understood him also at once. I saw a great deal of them both at that time, and rode about with them while Terrell was showing the Rajah the country around Burrator. The Rajah stayed at a well-known comfortable wayside inn, near Dartmoor, Dousland Barn it was then called, now unhappily rebuilt and renamed the Manor Hotel.

Terrell did not wish to sell his pretty moorland place, but he was no longer young, and, thinking of his wife and daughter, concluded that he could not refuse a large price for it. He therefore named a price which was about double what he had given for it. Good judge of land as he was, however, he did not realize the effect of railway communication on the value of land, and it was about the time when land was at its highest.

Although Burrator was six miles then from the nearest railway station, the land valuer sent down by the Rajah's trustees from London to value the place for the purchase, actually reported it to be worth more than Terrell had asked for it.

"The Rajah stayed at a well-known comfortable wayside inn, near Dartmoor, Dousland Barn it was then called, now unhappily rebuilt and renamed the Manor Hotel."

Terrell was therefore obliged to sell, and I think leaving Burrator was a great blow to him, from which he never recovered. But for some years he appeared to be the same as before. The Rajah stayed some time at Dousland Barn, whilst Terrell was preparing to leave Burrator. It was in the summer, and they rode together very often, Terrell showing the Rajah the country, and telling him what he should do. The Rajah had noticed the value of Terrell's opinion from the first, and they amused one another by their different ways of taking the world as they found it.

The Rajah was a grand man, with a grand manner of the right sort. There did not seem to be anything small or little about him. I do not hesitate to say he was a great man, and I believe historically he is so considered.

He was tall, lean, and upright in figure. He had scanty grey hair, with a high bald forehead, and his face, which had been goodlooking, was seared with confluent small pox, a disease he had suffered from in the eastern islands. His eyes were small, bright, and penetrating, but he had a softened mild expression of countenance that was exceedingly pleasant and attractive, though there was a lurking caution, to take care not to offend, to be found mingled with the rest. His voice was soft and mild, never hurried or excited, and he chose his words deliberately and well.

As the Rajah lived at Burrator some years, I saw a great deal of him while he was my neighbour, which he was until his death, and he certainly fully impressed me with his greatness as a man. He had suffered from paralysis, of which he had two or three attacks before his death, and he talked of their effects in his quiet fearless way. He was a great man struck down, but still great, ready to look his fate in the face whatever it might be.

Whilst at Burrator, and in a state of health he could not enjoy, he went twice to Sarawak to settle there his affairs, the second time to place the present Rajah in authority.

When recovering from an attack of paralysis he received me with his usual calm polite manner, and in a very quiet matter-of-fact way, said, "My tongue is not yet under complete control; if, therefore, I say what I cannot mean, if I say window instead of door, for instance, or use any unsuitable expression, you will know why." Then he proceeded with his usual pleasant conversation, and in fact made very few mistakes.

He died at Burrator, and lies buried in Sheepstor churchyard, under a red granite tomb, placed there by Lady Burdett-Coutts. The pretty little moorland church of the parish of Sheepstor was restored for his sake, by that lady chiefly, restored well, not destructively, and is now a monument to the Rajah's last days at Burrator.

The Rajah's talk with Terrell was most amusing, not to say instructive. Terrell gave him the best possible advice about living at Burrator, keeping cows, etc. And the Rajah answered any question Terrell put to him on any subject whatever in his usual good-tempered way. The conversation never flagged.

I heard Terrell say to him, "What sort of a thing's a Rajah?"

"Oh!" said the Rajah, "a kind of king." Terrell said, looking him all over, "'Every inch a king,' I'll warn* ee," quoting Shakespeare, with a Devonshire expression by way of emphasis.

Terrell was to turn out of Burrator, and, as he was going into a furnished house, he did not know what to do with all his old furniture, and other things which he had had about him all his life.

The Rajah asked him to make a list of everything in the house, put a price on each, and he would take what he wanted.

Everything that Terrell had was pretty good, though a good deal was old-fashioned. He made a full list, and put a value on the various things much on the principle of their value to him, whether he wished to keep them or not, putting high prices on whatever he did not want to part with, supposing the Rajah would be guided by the price. The Rajah just glanced his eye over the list, and, not wishing to be bothered with furnishing, said he would take it all.

Terrell said, "Stop! stop! I b'ant going to let you have my bed I was married in."

"Just as you please, Terrell," said the Rajah. And Terrell did as he pleased.

I did not lose Terrell as a near neighbour directly after he left Burrator. He settled for a time not far off. When he sold Burrator he expected to find another place that would suit him just as well, for not more than half the money he had got for it, but he never did, and he shifted from place to place, with an eye to being near the hounds. Although I saw a good deal of him by exchanging visits, meeting him in the hunting field and elsewhere, I did not see so much of him as before, nor so much as I should wish.

He settled for a time on the other side of the moor, nearer the Kennels, and liked, in the summer, to guide a party of young girls and men across the wild parts of the moor to his old haunts, or to meet me and a similar party at some choice spot. He liked a long ride, and I went with him one day twenty-five miles to see a horse, bred in a particular way through sire and dam, much to his fancy, and back again, but he did not buy the horse. He was good at long rides, and said a horse could go any distance at seven miles an hour, a hound trot, or jog trot. I should say six miles an hour.

The cream of Harry Terrell's life was spent at Burrator, and pity 'tis he sold it. But he thought it his duty to sell at a good price, as he considered himself a poor man, and he had a wife and daughter.

At Burrator he lived the life most genial to his tastes. He had a small farm of his own; poultry, always a game cock or two – very game indeed – always a good pony and a hunter, a good setter or two, and a first rate terrier, of course. Fishing and coursing were two sports that he did not care for; coursing because it was not hunting, and fishing because it was dull, and there was no company or "telling." He spent most of his time on Dartmoor, either on his pony, with his gun, setters, and terrier, or on his hunter.

* Devonshire for warrant.

94

I do not think Harry Terrell ever recovered leaving Burrator. He never settled down anywhere else, and he lost much of the comfort and tranquility of his life in his own Burrator, surrounded by woods and streams, intimate and familiar neighbours, in a part of the country where he was very well known. He went on hunting, but very gradually his health began to fail.

He lived longer, but he need not be followed to London, and to his grave; because from no fault or excess of his own, having always lived the halest of lives, he fell into ill health, and had to throw himself into the arms and under the loving care of his only child.

His health failed him when he was over sixty years old, and after hunting on until he was obliged to give it up, he retired to London, with his wife, to live with his married daughter. He lingered some little time, but was broken down. I went to see him there, and found that he expressed himself in his old strong humourous way, and his Devonshire dialect. He made me laugh, though it was sad to see him moping in a great city, when mountains, rivers, trees, flowers, birds, and beasts were his natural and favourite surroundings. He took his walks in a cemetery hard by, where there was something green, as he said, some grass, trees, and flowers, and where he was shortly to be laid at rest.

The Hostess said of Falstaff "a babbled of green fields" a touch of nature which must be Shakespeare's, let critics say what they please. There is nothing more to be said here, than to suggest that these really fine brains lead us often in the fall of life into distress, as if the machine were too delicate for the continual strain of activity which itself insists on.

Harry Terrell was born in Tavistock the 12th of April, 1807, and died in London the 18th of March, 1871.

"The Dartmoor pony is famous for his spirit and endurance." Ponies at Huccaby 1889.

Chapter Seven

A DARTMOOR COLT-DRIFT

H is Royal Highness the Prince of Wales, Duke of
Cornwall, is represented in the West of England
by the officials known as the Duchy of Cornwall,
or more commonly on Dartmoor as the Duchy. Once a
year the Duchy, in the observance of the duties of its
office, drives all the ponies on Dartmoor to a particular
spot, for the purpose of there and then levying fines on
their owners. The Venville tenants of the Duchy, who
have rights and are exempt from fines, are summoned to
the Drift to put in their claims; and this function of colt-
drift on the part of the Duchy has some picturesque, not
to say savage, features in it, which to a stranger not
broken in to Dartmoor manners and customs are as
striking as a war dance yet further West might be. The
Dartmoor pony is a wild beast, inhabiting that Forest in
great numbers, and has the peculiar faculty of living on
the waste from year's end to year's end without calling
on civilization for help, being in this regard more
independent even than the fox, who calls for geese,
ducks, and fowls from the cultured population in his
environment. The pony is a great wanderer in search of
pasture, and in the course of a few hours will exercise
rights of common on extensive tracts of land, respecting
neither forest boundaries nor parish boundaries, neither
Dukes of Cornwall nor lords of manors. By this free
roving life of his he has in his simple fashion, had his
influence in creating such a grand and fearful thing as
the law, having established rights which will probably be
the subject of argument in solemn courts before grave
and reverend judges. The rights of pasturage which he
enjoys are those of inter-commonage; and passing from

the Forest on to the commons of the surrounding parishes, and also from one common to another at his own sweet will, from generation to generation without let or hindrance, he has made for himself a legal position from which, it is to be hoped, no argument, however learned, will succeed in dislodging him.

The Duchy exercise some of the remnants of authority still left them of the old laws, amongst which is the colt-drift, the ponies being locally called colts, and they include in the drift not only their own Forest, but the commons adjacent also. Dartmoor is divided into four quarters, North, East, South, and West; and there is a functionary called par excellence a Moorman, who has charge of each quarter on behalf of the Duchy. The colt-drift takes place towards the end of August; but the particular day on which it is to happen is kept a profound secret, in order that the owners of ponies who have no rights on the moor may be caught trespassing, and fined five shillings. The Moorman is roused before dawn on the morning fixed upon for the drift by a messenger from headquarters; and he immediately proceeds, with others whom he calls to his assistance, mounted and on foot, accompanied by dogs, to drive every sort of horse on his quarter and the adjacent commons to, taking the Western quarter for an example, Merryvale Bridge, there to be claimed by their owners, or, if not claimed, to be driven to Dunnabridge pound – the Duchy pound – and sold at auction within three weeks if the owner does not put in an appearance. It was the ancient custom to proclaim the morn of the drift by the sounding of horns on the heights, and there is one particular stone in a commanding position, with a hole in it through which a horn was to be blown as a necessary part of the ceremony, that the Venville tenants might be wakened to a sense of their rights and attend the drift to claim their ponies. But the blowing of horns has fallen into disuse, and this idea on the part of the

"To drive every sort of horse to Merryvale Bridge, there to be claimed by their owners, or if not claimed to be driven to Dunnabridge pound." The entrance to Dunnabridge pound, 1892.

Duchy is an instance of the insolence of office and the oppressor's wrong that has to be borne in this weary world.

The Venville tenants are the parishioners of the parishes having commons adjoining the moor, and, all cattle and sheep apart, it is easy to see that the ponies, far famed for their many excellent qualities, ranging over the Forest and the commons indiscriminately from the beginning of time, have established rights for their owners which are good in law. The Venville tenants pay a Venville rent to the Duchy. What the word Venville means may one day be decided in the law courts, and we reserve our opinion on the subject till then, and enjoy rights of Venville therefore. It has been stated in old documents that it gives the right "to take everything off the Forest except vert (green oak) and red deer," which may be truly said to be a colourable pretext for taking everything, as neither red deer nor green oak can be found there. The Duchy, however, do not allow their own rights to lapse, and the colt-drift is one which they exercise with much form and ceremony, though they have unhappily left off the blowing of horns. The Venville tenants must, therefore, be on the lookout for the drift when the middle of August has gone by that they may claim their ponies, show that they are not of the wicked who are to be fined five shillings, and do a dilapidated sort of suit and service to their Venville lord. Some of the Venville tenants have of late raised an objection to the extension of the drift to their commons, contending that the Duchy have only the right to drive on their own Forest. This is a delicate question, and has led to a free fight between the assembled Venville tenants and the Duchy at Merryvale Bridge, accompanied by the use of language both loud and strong, which, seen and heard from the safe eminence of a neighbouring tor, adds considerably to the interest excited by the beauties of nature which deck the banks of the lovely Walkham river.

The colt-drift may well rank as a scene of most admired confusion, and he is a fortunate person who finds himself on Dartmoor on the chosen day, near enough to see and hear, but out of the danger of being himself included in the drift, and mixed with the crowd of ponies, dogs, Venville tenants, trespassers, and the Duchy at Merryvale Bridge. The first unwonted appearance that would attract his notice would be herds of wild rough ponies galloping over the moor and the tors in one direction, instead of quietly browsing in their customary manner in well-selected places, for your pony is a good judge of pasture. The Moorman has begun his drift early, and, with his driftmen in a line searching every corner that can hold a pony, is driving them all towards the time honoured place of assembly. The Dartmoor pony is famous for his spirit and endurance he is cleanlegged, with many of the characteristics of the thorough-bred horse, but with the small head, little short ears, excitable eyes, and long shaggy mane and tail peculiar to himself.

When galloping over the moor in a state of alarm, his mane and tail streaming in the breeze seem to be the principal part of him. In this state he is usually unbroken and shoeless, the period of his servitude to man not having as yet arrived, and he looks as wild and untamable as any traditional beast of the forest need be. The Venville tenants from their houses can see the unusual commotion on the hills above them, and proceed to Merryvale Bridge on tame ponies or on foot as the case may be. Other persons conscious of trespassing on the moor in the shape of ponies are also on the look-out, and throng to the drift to claim their property and be fined five shillings rather than go afterwards to Dunnabridge pound and pay expenses, as they are called, in addition. The scene at Merryvale Bridge thus becomes imposing. A vast number of these wild-looking ponies are huddled together in a small space, the bed of the river itself being full of them. Venville tenants have come not only to claim their property, but also to protest in very choice Dartmoor English against the drift on their own commons outside the Forest bounds, and they make an attempt, which seems hopeless, to drive the ponies from such commons back again to their own ground. An official of the Duchy makes a proclamation from the top of a granite boulder, and ceremoniously reads a document with great seals attached to it to the assembled multitude. After that formality has been observed, the claiming, the wrangling, the protesting, and the fining follow, with much loss of temper, some loss of sobriety – for the "Dartmoor Inn" is hard by – and a marked relaxation of the refinement and gentleness of manner that a rough life on Dartmoor might be expected to impart.

Merryvale Bridge is one of the most picturesque places in Devonshire. It spans the river Walkham in a deep valley, where the water flows rapid and foaming over a granite bed, and some of the highest tors on Dartmoor, with Mist Tor as their monarch, look down on it. Down stream Vixen Tor may be seen, a wonderful pile of rocks famous in romantic print for its Druids; a dense coppice succeeds when the enclosed country is reached. On rising ground above are stone circles, a stone avenue, and a cromlech, which have exercised the ingenuity of many an antiquary; and close to the Bridge are a few cottages, with the "Dartmoor Inn," forming a hamlet, the green in front of which, sloping down to the river, is the final and stirring scene of the drift. Among the other incidents which happen, the catching of a pony is worthy of attention. There is always a boy ready to undertake the task; and the pony being at a disadvantage, hemmed in by the herd, the boy goes for him, and, laying hold of his long mane and forelock, hangs on until he gives in, which the pony is in no hurry to do, as he fights hard, especially with his handy forefeet, using them with more effect even than a kick with the hinder ones will produce.

The Duchy exercise this right of drift, and many other rights, but do not seem to recognise the principle that duties accompany rights in nearly all cages. The colt-drift might be made an exceedingly useful exercise of authority by regulating through its means the breeding of these valuable little steeds, and by keeping trespassers off the Forest and the common pasturage, which by right belongs to the Duchy tenants and the commoners in Venville. If the Duchy did their duty, no one would complain, and they might perform the right of drift with all the solemnity so fitting to the occasion without a row, the grievance of omitting to blow horns in the proper places according to ancient custom being easily remedied. Fining strangers five shillings for having ponies where they have no right to pasture them is beneath the dignity of the Duchy if the matter ends there and no useful duty be done. Then there is, besides, the burning question of the enclosures on the Forest. The enclosures that have been authorised by the Duchy are encroachments on the free pasturage, which is very hard on the ponies. The Duchy talk of limited common – that is, right of common limited to the number of cattle which can be kept on the farms in Venville around the Forest through the winter. But this question of limited common, though it may be law, has never been decided in the courts, and no man can say what it may be held to be. The ponies, which cost less and are worth more than the cattle, weight for weight, useful and pretty little beasts, though wild on the moor, docile at home, good hacks, strong and tough in harness, the joy of all boys who can ride them, care not a rap for winter quarters, and the law of limited common would not touch their case at all. They have, however, a natural taste for good pasturage and occasionally shelter in warm valleys when the winds and the snow make revel on the moors; and the lives of hundreds are sacrificed by taking the best pasture and the snug combes from these little palfreys on the poor plea of limited common – limited, indeed, with a vengeance.

May happier times come to these companions and friends of man, who play such a leading part in the dramatic spectacle known as the Dartmoor Colt-drift!

Members of the South Devon Hunt with fox hounds on show, 1920s.

Chapter Eight

A FOXHOUND PUPPY SHOW

The foxhound cult – not to say it profanely, but with reverence for whatever a man sets his mind to do with his whole heart and soul, making not a religion of it, but an object for himself and fellow-men to idolize rather than to worship – has been the special study of the English country gentleman.

It is given to us, or to some of us, to admire many of the animals that nature has put in our way, and she has certainly, with her fine taste, strewn things of beauty in pleasant places to tell us, or some of us, what the beautiful should be thought to be. But it is the ambition of art to improve upon her teaching, and to surpass nature in matters of taste. Take the theme of our praise, the foxhound, by no means a child of nature, what has she ever done to equal this work of art, gained by generations upon generations of careful, thoughtful, and tasteful breeding from the common dog of nature's workshop?

There is no need to trace the history of the foxhound from the beginning, through his many and various changes, to tell of a Puppy Show; but the solemn conclave of Worldly Wisemen which goes by that name – a name not, indeed, correct, but a sort of technical term – has very much to do with the foxhound cult, as will presently be seen.

The sire and dam of a foxhound are selected with the care and with the minute observation of special qualities which the English squire has so conspicuously displayed in the breeding of the wonderful animals that he, and he alone it would appear, has set before the admiring gaze of the world. When the foxhound is born he is called a whelp, and is entrusted to the care of his dam until he is about two months old. At this age he is promoted to the rank of puppy, is named with a name that should begin with the same letter with which the name of his sire or dam begins, to call to memory the parent for whose particular excellence he or she was selected, and he is sent out. It is well to explain kennel terms, for they may not be known to some, who nevertheless like to hear about a puppy show. When a foxhound puppy is sent out a kind friend of the hunt takes charge of him and walks him. He is sent out to walk. When a puppy is sent out to walk he does not go with a nursery-maid to the park, but he goes from the kennels to a house in the country, where he is well fed, has plenty of fresh air, and is allowed full liberty to play any pranks he pleases. It is well that two puppies should be sent out together to play with one another, as they are not so apt, in that case, to pull everything to pieces that they can get hold of; including a few chickens and other small deer, by way of amusement. Their gambols and their frolics are quite delightful, and if they pull up a rose or two in your garden, or find their way to your dressing-room and tear your sponge to pieces, or when wet and weary lie on your sofa in the drawing-room, it is right to remember that they are foxhounds, to be future members of a famous pack, and are, by virtue of the cult, as sacred beasts as any Brahmin bull ever was. The fox-hound is usually whelped, to use the proper term, from February to May – that is, during the first four spring months. He is sent out when two months old, and he is sent in – returned to the kennels – about the February following, when he is eight to twelve months old. From some kennels sixty couples of puppies, or so, may be sent out each year to their walks. They are subject to diseases that are often fatal – the yellows, a sort of jaundice, and the distemper – and of the sixty couples no more than forty or fifty couples may be sent in. Then comes the puppy show.

The usual season for puppy shows, which is a festival in every kennel, is the time between the end of the hunting season in the spring and the beginning of the cub-hunting season in the autumn, when the pack must be made up ready for the field. Drafts and entries must be made into and out of the pack for the coming season, on the joint judgment of the master and the huntsman; drafts from the old pack replaced by entries of young hounds, according to the known faults of the one and the expected merits of the other. Drafts and entries are kennel terms that hardly require explanation.

The puppies when they are sent in are no longer puppies, and are, properly speaking, young hounds, with none of the puppy character about them. They are then submitted to the judgment of the wisest men to be found, who may be, for example, a well-known authority on hounds and hunting, a very wily old huntsman, and a third, perhaps, a master of hounds from a distant pack, that there may always be two to one when doubts arise. The master and huntsman of the pack in question have not a word to say, and stand aloof; for the hounds are to be judged without prejudice. They can only be judged at a puppy show in the matter of their make and shape, which are of the greatest importance; their noses, their tongues, the pace they can carry on in a chase, and their hunting qualities in general come to be judged by the master and huntsman afterwards. Neither do the judges take notice of colour. If a master has a fancy for colour, as modern masters all have, many and many a good whelp is drafted for his colour, and this fancy costs the pack excellent hounds. Uniformity of colour looks well; and when the chosen colour is the Belvoir tan, now the fashion – nothing can well be handsomer.   As the master, huntsman, and servants know all the hounds, however uniform their colour, there may be an advantage in the field in general not knowing them, as they cannot then talk nonsense on the merits of particular hounds. Taking the pack as a thing of beauty, with some other advantages, perhaps the taste for colour, though it costs a great deal, may be pronounced right. The judges have the young hounds brought before them – a couple or so at a time – the dogs (that term being only used to denote sex) first, and the bitches afterwards; or they may prefer the bitches first, as the dogs are larger, and may put the bitches in the shade. They take infinite trouble in judging the hounds as a whole, and in awarding six prizes – three to the dogs, first, second, and third, and three to the bitches. The prizes go to those who have walked the puppies, and though the amount is small, quite enough, however, to reward a careful servant – there is great rivalry and pride in winning a prize for such a favourite as the puppy has been. Good feeding and good management have much to do with the good growth of all young things, and the prizes are an inducement for rivalry in such matters. But when the huntsman sends the puppies out he can make a shrewd guess as to which will make the finest hounds when sent in, and will be inclined to favour those who walk them the best, and have for that reason a double advantage.

The points of a foxhound need not be given here; are they not written in every book that ever was published on hunting? And yet, with all the book-learning, good judges of hounds are rare.

The puppy show, it will thus be seen, plays an important part in the great foxhound cult. Generations on generations of hounds have passed through the solemn ordeal of a trial of their merits in form and symmetry by picked judges. And from generation to generation the best have been bred from the best, reaching as near to perfection as possible in such a world as this. So important is form, which includes all the details known as the points in a hound, that no master would enter a shapeless hound or keep him in his pack, however good a hunter he may be. In fact, an ill-shaped hound cannot go the pace, or stay a distance, and cannot enter a pack of fame. It needs no effort of the imagination to see that in a hundred years, which may include twenty-five to thirty generations, about the time that the modern foxhound has been bred from ancestors of a more ancient type, careful and studied selection has given us a very beautiful animal indeed. The foxhound has been bred for his beauty in form and colour; also for his sagacity, his nose, his tongue, his strength, and his fleetness. And at a puppy show he is to be seen in the pride and perfection of young maturity, with all the bloom, brightness, and gaiety of youth; for he is, in truth, no longer a puppy, but a hound. He may not as yet have been rounded. His long, flowing, handsome ears, which so well set off his fine head and his dark soft-looking eyes, have not been cut shorter and round with an instrument made for the purpose, to save them from being torn in the chase by briars and thorns. Some packs of hounds are now spared this infliction. A ragged and torn ear in an old hound does not look well, but if in modern hunting the risk of such injuries is lessened, the hound will look all the better in his own natural ears.

Puppy shows are held at the kennels, and besides the judges, the wise and learned are bid, who assemble, judge the judges and their judgments, and in select conclave take note of what puppies have answered to their breeding, and draw conclusions as to what sort of pack the next season will bring forth in the field. These, though they be of the select, are not consulted in the judging, nor in the entering and drafting to make the pack, which, after all, is the exclusive concern of the master and huntsman; but as they say nothing they think the more, and it is a day of thorough enjoyment and satisfaction to such as they.

Other puppy shows are more festive, and sometimes they assume the proportions of a fete of a very gay nature. Imagine, for instance, a lawn tennis ground near the mansion of the master, and not far from the kennels. The whole hunt with their wives and daughters are bidden to the feast of reason and otherwise. The place is beautiful, the ground railed off; with a low platform in the middle for the judges, and for the hounds under judgment and measurement. The young hounds in all their glory are paraded by their intimate friends who had walked them. The young heir of the house, a four-year-old infant Hercules, is entrusted with a good-natured young hound, parading with the rest in great triumph. To the mind of a happy person endowed with the gifts of a devotee of the foxhound cult, nothing could be more enchanting or inspiring than this not imaginary festival. Luncheon and champagne might be found hard by, somewhere in the mansion; but puppy shows being, as described, very solemn things in themselves, such vanities may be mentioned only to be despised.

Praise be to that beautiful creature the foxhound. He is caviare to the general. But to know him is to know the most charming of companions, loving, intellectual, gay, and comely.

Chapter Nine

CUB-HUNTING

The sport of fox-hunting offers infinite variety to those who devote themselves to that amusement or, as it used to be called in old stories and songs, diversion. The fox-hunter must take his pleasure seriously, or he is no fox-hunter. He may go out with the hounds six days a week, ride to hounds well and gallantly on the finest of horses, dress himself to perfection, be the prince of good fellows, and yet be no fox-hunter in the eyes of the true fox-hunting squire. The true fox-hunter is a country gentleman, who lives on his estates, hunts with the hounds of his own country every time they go out, no matter what the weather is, often also with other packs, never uses the steam covert-hack if he can help it, but rides his own covert-hacks long distances, and looks upon his sport as one of the most important duties of his life, which is no play, but downright hard work, that rejoiceth him even as such. The year is divided for him into the fox-hunting season; the summer season, when he takes the keenest interest in hearing about puppies at walk, in knowing where vixens have put down their cubs, in the Puppy Show, and in the colts that have to be broken; and the cub-hunting season.

Cub-hunting is not fox-hunting, and if it is taken on its own merits, quite apart from any other form of diversion, it is one of the prettiest sports imaginable.

The vixen puts down her cubs about the month of May, and has to teach them their country and the way to get their own living between that time and the first or second week in August, when they are fine young foxes with very fluffy fur, which makes them look fresh and handsome. Some think that the fox helps the vixen in this arduous task; but, as the vixen is very shy in putting down her cubs, often in shallow out-of-the-way places, removing them as soon as they are old enough to the larger and safer earths, it is open to doubt whether the fox condescends to notice them at all. Judging by analogy with other beasts of the field, it is likely that he knows not the joys or the cares of parental affection.

The huntsman, having made up his pack after the Puppy Show, and completed his drafts and entries, is anxious to begin teaching his young hounds and preparing them for the hunting season, and that is the main object of cub-hunting. Another object is not only to teach young hounds what a fox means, but also to teach young foxes what a hound means, in which double process many a cub, and possibly a young hound or two, lose their lives. A favourite puppy of our acquaintance got on the line of an old fox with a few old hounds in cub-hunting, ran a long distance, came back to the kennel about thirty hours afterwards, and died of exhaustion. The old hounds were none the worse, as with them it was not an uncommon occurrence. Condition in hound or horse is everything.

Cub-hunting begins as soon as the harvest is over, as hounds, to say nothing of horses, going through standing corn are supposed to injure the almighty farmer. But, if the harvest is very late, the outlying wild districts and the great woodlands are resorted to. The cub-hunting season may be said to begin as early as convenient in August, and end with the last days of October, after which the first fox-hunting meets are published. Cub-hunting proper is a quasi-mystery. The meets are not published, and have the air of being a secret trysting-place of the master, the huntsman, and the whips. The servants wear their last-season scarlet, as the hounds know them better in that colour. Others dress as they please; but the good dresser has his cub-hunting suit of neat top-boots, brown breeches, and dark coat. There always appear at the meet some old hunting hands with profound wisdom expressed on their countenance, as if inspiration had led them to the spot, of whom our hunting squire is sure to be one. This is in the early and creamy days of cub-hunting before it ripens into fox-hunting, which it gradually does towards the end of October.

To enjoy cub-hunting is not to enjoy one's bed. The huntsman at break of day takes out a very large pack of mixed, young and old, hounds, and meets his master at the appointed place, which would be near a covert wherein litters of cubs are known to be. His young hounds as yet are strangers to the fox, but are full of life, fun, and frolic, and have, when out at walk, been hunting anything they pleased. A hound, with such an exquisite nose as he has, must hunt something. Now they have to learn not only what a fox is, but what everything else is not. The young hounds have a tendency to follow the huntsman as their particular friend; but he knows that the spirit within them will not allow them to remain quiet, he therefore makes himself as dull and silent as possible. If he hustled about, blowing his horn, and craming to the front, the young hounds would think it good fun of itself. But as he remains very quiet after having sent the old hounds into the covert, the young hounds vote it dull, and are eager to go to the first tongue they hear just to see what is going on. Soon the hounds open in full chorus, and the cubs are scattered all over the covert; the old foxes have gone away by virtue of their experience of last season, and if a few hounds get on their line they are stopped by the whips. A cub soon falls a victim to his want of knowledge of the world, and the young hounds learn what blood is. A great fuss is made over the body of the dead cub to impress the young hounds with the idea that these funereal rites are the main objects of life.

Our squire gets up at an early hour and rides his quiet old cub-hunter, one of his hacks, a cob, or a pony, either to the meet or the covert to be first drawn, and knowing the sport, the country, and every hound in the pack, thoroughly enjoys in the early autumn the quiet and deliberate process, comparatively, of entering the young hounds to their game. The sport consists in observing the young hounds and the cubs, and not in riding to hounds at a great pace. There is no eager anxiety to get through your field, and cram to the front at all risks, that you may have a chance to see the run, when the man who does not know how to get a good start, or to recover lost ground, is hopelessly out of a good thing. All the anxiety, care, etiquette, and sometimes the vexation, to say nothing of the fatal jealousy, of fox-hunting is absent. Cub-hunting is a calm, leisurely sport, when nature is very beautiful, the flowers are still in bloom, the sun shines warm, and the coverts are dense with leaf. There is no crowd of horsemen, and no ladies for whom it is necessary to open a gate; and, in addition to such negative charms, our Squire, who knows every path and every gate, notwithstanding that silence is golden in cub-hunting, enjoys a quiet chat with the master about the young entries, admires the form of Hector, the dash of Romulus, and the tongue of Harmony, prize-winners at the Puppy Show. The charm of cub-hunting consists in the quiet enjoyment of the mere hunting of young hounds, chiefly in covert, following their own instincts, but taking their lessons from the older hounds, their encouragements from the huntsman, and their ratings by way of reproof from the whips. They are severely stopped from riot – that is hare, rabbit, &c – but whipcord is used more for its sound than its sting. The whips, however, are to teach the young idea that their natural foods – hare, rabbit, sheep, deer – are unworthy of notice, and the fox alone is fit to regale their delicate noses.

The hunting-man in the country learns a great deal

in cub-hunting that is useful to him in fox-hunting. If he goes out regularly he will know where the foxes are to be found, and their running; the same fox will usually take the same line in the same season. He will know the changes that have taken place in the country during the summer, when the riding-paths in coverts have been altered by growth or by cutting, for example, and he will learn how best to get through a difficult bit of country, or where the huntsman crosses a bad place. True cub-hunting is to be found in the early part of the season; as the young hounds enter it gradually grows into fox-hunting; more people appear at the covert side, especially as the time of meeting gets later, and towards the end of October it assumes more the character of fox-hunting, and a good fox may be run. We hold, however, that to run a good fox in cub-hunting is not the right thing. In cub-hunting the shortrunning foxes should be killed, the more the better, and the good foxes should be left for the great sport. Gamekeepers like to see foxes killed in cub-hunting. One of their wiles is to get rid of the old foxes, and feed the cubs themselves with rabbits, &c.; in this way the cubs get fat, comparatively tame, know no country but their own native covert, and fall easy victims to a large cub-hunting pack. The keeper is then rewarded for the number of cubs he has shown, having removed the parents, who would have taught them their cunning. Huntsmen and keepers are apt to shift litters – to take them out from one place and put them down in another more convenient perhaps for both – which entails artificial feeding, and the loss of the vixen's lessons in wisdom. A fox once handled, according to Jack Russell, is no good for two years.

In the great hunting Shires the whole fox-hunting proceeding is more or less ceremonious, occasioned by the number of people who take part in it for many various reasons, and it is almost reduced to riding to hounds. In the outlying provinces there is still to be found hunting for hunting's sake. In the Shires the cub-hunter is a horse used for that purpose, and the hunter is kept and trained for the fox-hunting season. In the provinces the hunter is often taken out to get gradually into condition by sober cub-hunting for long hours, and we venture to think the condition of hunters is better understood sometimes in the provinces by a good sportsman with a horse or two, for instance, trained by himself, than it is in the Shires, where there are second horsemen out, where hunters are trained by the grooms, and where there are all sorts of such-like luxuries.

The cub-hunting season is now over, and the young hounds and the young foxes are both well fitted for the fox-hunting season, when neither are any longer considered or talked of as youthful. The cubs are foxes, and know to their cost the sound of the huntsman's horn, and the puppies are hounds only known by a few to be in their first season; they have assumed all the airs and manners of the older hounds.

Chapter Ten

THE TONGUE OF THE HOUND

T
he tongue of the foxhound, uttered as it is in the wilds of a hunting country, resounding in the valleys, awakening the echoes in the cliffs, chiming over the uplands, or making the woodlands ring with music, far from the madding crowd, away from the music-hall, or stage-play, is one of the most melodious and spirit-stirring strains that can be heard in the world of sound. How came he by this tuneful tongue? It is as distinct in melody from the bark of a dog as anything well can be that is similar in its kind. We all know that a hound is not a dog, except as he may be so classified by the zoologist. The man who knows and loves his hound only uses the word dog, as he does the word bitch, to denote sex. He has his dog-hound and his bitch-hound, his dog-pack and his bitch-pack of hounds. In latter days these different packs have come to be called the large pack and the small pack; dogs being usually an inch or two higher than bitches – a small dog of value, the word dog only indicating sex, is put into the bitch-pack.

But whence did this fine tongue come? Darwin tells us that no dog barked before he was domesticated, and, considering that the fox is classified with the dog, it is rather surprising that he should say so, for the fox in his wild state undoubtedly barks. Who, amongst fox-hunters, has not heard the short bark of the fox, calling for his mate, early in the morning of the balmy spring, telling the listener as he lies with his window open not far from a thick covert, that the sacred beast has not been sacrificed to save the souls of pheasants or keepers? The bark of a fox is exactly that of a small terrier, though a little shorter, and not shrill.

But whence did the fine tongue of the hound come? Who says the English are not a musical nation? Mr Baring-Gould declares that they are but that their minstrels were suppressed by Henry VIII and his stern daughter, Elizabeth. It is odd that the English hound, alone of hounds, should have this melodious tongue. The Basset hound has a common bark, no better than a spaniel's, for he is French; yet he is in personal appearance very like the beagle of Bewick's pencil, whose tongue was melody itself. It must have been of the beagle that Shakespeare wrote

Their heads are hung
With ears that sweep away the morning dew;
Crook-kneed, and dew-lap'd like Thessalian bulls;
Slow in pursuit, but matched in mouth like bells,
Each under each. A cry more tunable
Was never holla'd to, nor cheer'd with horn.

There was feeling for music in those days. Shakespeare was a hunter, bred in the purlieus of the forest, and the charm of forest music must have possessed him, for whose verse was ever so musical as his? How is it, then, that the Basset hound speaks the speech of a common dog, and the beagle of old sang a chant? How is it that the dachshund, of German origin, talks like a dog, and the beagle, harrier, and foxhound intone their praise of nature?

In the early days of hunting, the stag, or rather the hart – a name improperly gone out of use – was the chief beast of the forest, and the pride, pomp, and circumstance of the glorious chase attended his taking and his death. But the hart was shot by an arrow from the bow, and the stricken deer was run down by gaze-hounds hounds at gaze

Why, let the stricken deer go weep,
The hart ungalled play.

To run a quarry with hounds having tongues to proclaim the track of his foot was an afterthought, and probably had its origin in running the hare with beagles. In the vast forests of Europe a line-hunter on the scent of an ungalled hart would be lost to all eternity. It is in England alone that the culture, which may almost be called a cult, of this hound's tongue could have grown into a sort of passion. And it is the much-scorned foxhunting squire of the last century, Undeservedly scorned by the votaries of another culture different from his, whose fine taste may be detected in the tongue of his hound, in his old mansions, in his gardens, his parks, his woods, and in country life as it is followed in England, who took pains to produce his foxhounds.

The hound has been bred by him for very many generations. The old beagle, the old slow line-hunting staghound, the harrier, and the modern foxhound have been bred with infinite care, like his sheep and his cattle, affording such a man as Darwin examples and evidence on which to found scientific theories. It must have been long ago that the hound's tongue took his fancy, for no hound ever condescends to a common bark now. Such a vulgar thing must have been bred out of him for generations on generations. In so-called puppy shows nowadays, when the young hounds sent into the kennels are judged on their merit in shape and form, the tongue is not heard or judged any more than the pace or hunting qualities can be then judged. But no one for an instant would doubt that the hound would have his or her tuneful tongue, soon to be known to the huntsman's ear as surely as, or more surely than, the form, style, and colour are known to his eye. In the hound the note of the dog is different from the note of the bitch, as every huntsman knows; but it is all melody, and, when a single hound opens on scent, doubling his tongue, as some do, in a manner not unlike the jodel of the Swiss, the heart of the foxhunting squire rejoiceth, and the music of the woods and the fields is an inspiration. Let not the culture of the cities despise the tastes generated in the fields. It is a taste, fresh, manly, vigorous, and sweet withal. The memory of the tongue of Sontag in a certain pack is very wild and sweet, as the memory of the voice of the greater Sontag, from whom she took her name, still sounds in one's ear as that of a saint in music.

The hound's tongue is a curious fact, and must have been the reward of careful breeding, we say in England, where heredity has been so much the guide of men, to enchant the musical ear of a musical nation. Hounds are said to sing in their kennels, and huntsmen who fear that quarrels may arise are recommended, on the authority of the Badminton Library, to let them sing. In hunting it was a necessity that hounds should be heard, and that the tongues of the hounds should vary, that the huntsman should know who spoke, and the hounds themselves should know the tongue of truth from that of the youthful babbler, and go to it. It would seem that this wild and beautiful cry from the woodlands has arisen partly from the necessities of the modern chase; but surely also from the musical instincts of the hunting man of England. "Nimrod," in *The Horse and the Hound*, quotes Addison's Knight turning a hound that had been given to him as an "excellent bass" whereas the note he wanted was a "counter tenor". And this is a hint how the squires of bygone times valued the tongues of their hounds. The variety of note in a pack of foxhounds is very great but it is all musical, and stirs the spirit of the man, and even of his horse, to deeds of daring that the fascinating cry may not die away in the distance, and be lost to him left in the rear.

The common names of hounds – Chauntress, Chorister, Clarinet, Concord, Dulcimer, Echo, Harmony,

Lullaby, Madrigal, Melody, Monody, Music, Musical, Sappho, Songster, Songstress, Sontag, Symphony, Tunable, Tuneful, Violin, Vocal, Voluble – of themselves enchant the ear, and so delicate does the ear of a huntsman become, that a slight variation in the note of a hound announcing uncertainty from a babbler, tells him that the hound has been too free with his tongue on riot (the hunting term for the scent of the wrong animal).

Hunting, like other things, has undergone its changes. Fields of hunting and riding men are very large. Many hunt to ride, rather than ride to hunt, and much of the downright interest in hunting is lost in the madding crowd of riding men. But in the wild, outlying countries, away from the Shires, as they are called, there is hunting still, and a select field who know the hounds. The tongue of the hound is as charming as ever it was; but how many of the modern hard-riding men are deaf to the voice of the charmer, charm he never so wisely?

The Hound and the Horn. The huntsman and his hounds at the South Devon meet on Manaton Green c.1900

Chapter Eleven

THE HOUND AND HORN*

The life of a great huntsman is a good theme for a sportsman, and this daintily got-up little book has a very tempting appearance. George Carter was born and bred in the "most high and palmy days" of fox-hunting, the first forty years of this century, before railways not only altered the face of the country, but changed the tone of country life altogether. Those were the days of horsemanship, when the horse was the only locomotive, when to be a horseman and to know something about horses was a necessity to an active life, and stagnation, both mental and physical, was the only alternative. Pace was quickening, possibly it always has been quickening. Fox-hunting took the place of the hare-hunting of Squire Western's days, and the wonderfully fast coaches of fifty years ago superseded the slow stages of the eighteenth century. In the year 1840 George Carter was forty-eight years old, and had passed the prime of life, as the palmy days of fox-hunting had passed or were passing. He died when he was within seven days of ninety-two years of age; and this "Life and Recollections," beyond a mere record of dates, consists of reports of the gossip of an old man at his fireside, full of wise saws and modern instances. A huntsman of his eminence must have been a very clever man, and he is reported to have had a very fine memory. Everybody knows that to be a really good huntsman, or to be a Prime Minister, demands both these qualities, though it would never do for a huntsman to be dismissed every five years or so by a fickle majority after the manner of Prime Ministers. George Carter, like

---

* *The Hound and Horn; or, Life and Recollections of George Carter, the Great Huntsman.* London: Simpkin, Marshall & Co. 1885.

many another good huntsman, was first entered to hare-hunting, an abomination to the true fox-hunter, who very properly holds that very inferior so-called sport in supreme contempt. But a truly great mind, such as fox-hunting requires, can reject the bad lessons learnt in the hare-hunting field, and retain only the good ones, few though they may be. He flourished in the days when fox-hunting squires rode many miles to covert on a galloping hack, or relays of covert hacks, whilst their poorer brethren, often the better sportsmen, possibly by virtue of their poverty, patiently rode their hunters on to covert at a slow hound trot. In the days when finding a fox was an art, and a drag on which hounds feathered but on no account spoke was a welcome thing to a huntsman – in the days when the field was much smaller in numbers than fields now are, and were expected to know something about their sport – in the days when port wine circulated on polished mahogany after dinner, and runs, hounds, and horses were inexhaustible topics for talk most fascinating and delightful to those who understood the tongue, what could not a man like George Carter, who had a fine memory, have told of all this!

The hunting-field is nothing if it is not amusing. It must be very amusing even now when the railway brings crowds of strangers to the covertside, when every covert is expected to hold a fox or two, and the chase is a mere race across country. It is hunting, no doubt, but there is much less of real downright hunting than there used to be, and as to woodcraft there is no longer any call for it. The hounds are perfection, if there is such a thing; so are the horses, and the riding is as good as ever; but the hunting is gone, and with it the pleasures attending the gratification of an instinct in a hunting animal. The closest intimacy and goodfellowship sprang up in the good old hunting days between those who constantly rode miles with one another to covert, by short cuts, through by-ways, and over lands which the red coat and top-boots passed free from the reproach of trespass. At certain points certain friends would join as surely as the rising of the sun, and at the meet, with the punctuality of fox-hunters, horsemen would appear from all points of the compass wending their way to the one place on the earth of absorbing interest to them; perhaps a desolate moorland spot, suddenly enlivened by horn, hounds, horses, and men, greetings and laughter and gorgeous dress, in the course of twenty minutes again to relapse into desolation and silence. The freedom of talk was great, and the wit and humour unrestrained by the presence of strangers. One or two such might appear, were immediately judged to be sportsmen or not by their behaviour on arrival, by their seat on their horse, or even by how their boots were put on, and as strangers they were given welcome. The huntsman was a great man, the greatest of servants, as he still is, but not inaccessible, and words of wisdom about hounds and hunting might be obtained from him without outraging the decencies of life. In the modern field of one to three hundred, with many strangers, and wild men from the depths of the cities, the huntsman must be let alone, and his mind left undisturbed by irresponsible frivolities. Everybody knew, in those good old days, what everybody else said or did, and might dispute the sayings and doings, too, in any language he might select as most appropriate for his purpose; and there was a charm in the great range of ideas and their expression to which this freedom from the restraints of classical or parliamentary language gave rise. The amusement of fox-hunting is certainly still very great to those who take pains to qualify themselves for its enjoyment, and all amusements must be understood to be enjoyed; but it cannot be now what it was to the country squire, who after a public school and the University, lived a retired life, devoted himself to sport, and became more and more eccentric as the memories of Eton and Oxford faded, or assumed the fantastic forms which memories are apt to take as they lapse into imagination. The fox-hunting squire was often a man of wit, humour, pathos, and refinement, not to be held up to scorn, as he has too often been, as an ignorant, inarticulate boor. He was independent of the world, cared not for its praise or blame, and went his own way, developing his own ideas, and living a robust life both physically and mentally. He formed lasting friendships at the covert-side, and loved his friends heartily. So far from familiarity breeding contempt, according to the copy-books, it bred infinite jest and fun, and the hunting day, ending with the port wine on the polished mahogany, was a day of intense pleasure, not only in the hunting and its adventures, but in the saying of everything that entered the head in any language that was most handy, an eccentric idea being pretty sure of an eccentric reception.

To sit down for a couple of hours with Jack Russell was to know what sort of amusement the hunting field might afford. George Carter was for many years huntsman to the famous Assheton Smith, a very odd man, as George Carter himself calls him.

There is a pleasant photographic portrait of George Carter in his old age facing the title-page, in his hunting costume (minus his spurs), and coloured. It is a gay-looking little book, and the good old huntsman certainly deserved the compliment of its publication. It is a record of a faithful life, and should be on the shelves of those who esteem such lives.

Chapter Twelve

FOX-HUNTING ON DARTMOOR

Hunting the wild red-deer on Exmoor has become the fashion of late – too much the fashion, perhaps, to make it a very sporting affair; but a fine September spent with the stag-hounds is a delightful way of seeing and enjoying that beautiful country. One of the greatest charms of hunting is, that you are led by the chase into sundry and out-of-the-way places, sometimes of great beauty, which would never be seen except by the few who live hard by, with whom familiarity may have bred contempt. To know a large tract of country as well as a hunting-man knows his country, to know every path, every stream, every ford, every lane, every gate, to say nothing of all the intricacies of the woodlands, is of itself a joy exclusively given to him. If hunting falls before the scythe of the Destroyer, this knowledge, amongst the rest, will be lost; the red-deer and the wild fox will be as the wild cat, the tree martin, the eagle, and the peregrine falcon, beautiful animals gone from us for ever-extinguished in the name of humanity. It would be a curious study in comparative psychology to speculate whether a fox would prefer life with hunting to no life at all as a man doubtless prefers life with the gout to obliteration. As the wild red-deer is to Exmoor, so is the wild fox, the old aboriginal large grey fox, to Dartmoor. And if you want to know Dartmoor as it ought to be known, scorning guide-books and antiquarian researches into Druidical remains which the freaks of nature have bountifully supplied for the dilettanti, you must hunt this fox. You must not refrain from following after him; and where he goeth you must go, even unto the bogs. Getting into a bog on horseback causes a curious sensation that no man who has any respect for science ought to neglect. We have given up limiting ourselves to five senses, and a sixth has been authoritatively announced. If a philosopher could be induced to hunt the fox on Dartmoor, he would experience an entirely new sensation, utterly unlike any other, when he rode his horse into a bog, which he would be bound to announce as a seventh. It is an old tradition, and a well-known fact, that no man or horse was ever hurt in a bog, though it must be allowed that it requires an educated taste, as in the case of Wagner's music and some curious old wines, to like it. It is the necessity for a good education that makes hunting on Dartmoor, very fortunately, not so popular as it might be. But to the past master, the man who has come out in honours, what hunting can be compared to it? It is true that you may take a very high degree in Leicestershire and find yourself at the bottom of the class, if a bog may be made classical, at the university of Dartmoor; and this, no doubt, carries with it its vexations. To lead the field with the Quorn, and have to follow a roughish-looking moorman, albeit very well mounted, with the Dartmoor hounds is humiliating. But everybody knows that humility is a very good thing, and it is not less so in fox-hunting than in any other walk, or gallop, in life. To run one of these great grey foxes from the large coverts at Stowford Cleave, on the Erme, near Ivybridge, across the moor to the still larger coverts at Benjay Tor, on the Dart, near Holne Chase, ten miles off; is the perfection of hunting to a really hunting-man who is not a common rider to hounds. The vice of the present day and of the present system is that large, unmanageable fields have reduced huntingmen to mere riders, and woodcraft is like to become a lost art. There has been a revival of hunting in this 'so-called' nineteenth century, as there have been other revivals; and hunting has its ritualists as well as other more solemn institutions. The vestments are gay and lively; the tall hat, the neat tie, the scarlet coat, the white leather breeches, the top-boots, and the spurs, with every buckle and button in the right place, make a cheerful sight on Dartmoor with a pack of hounds, and set off the scenery with great effect. But the ritualism or etiquette of the modern field is a damper to hunting. Not to know the names of the bounds, not to know their tongues, not to know their different merits in drawing or in chase, with a huntsman as a high-priest of the mysteries, is a misery which civilization has happily as yet spared Dartmoor. Sir Francis Grant once said to Count d'Orsay, "That was a fine run." "Run!" said d'Orsay, "it was an epic poem."

Such is a run from Stowford Cleave to Benjay Tor. The first stave is sung by Susan. She has already signalled to the huntsman by a feather of her stern that the fox is there, and the fox's delicate ear has caught a warning sound. He has moved at once from his kennel, and soon Susan proclaims him on foot, doubling her tongue in a high-pitched key, like the utterance of a wild cry of delight. He has heard Susan's tongue before and Sontag's, her dam's, too, for that matter, a season or two ago, and although you may call it music, he thinks it Billingsgate, and puts her down as a common scold; no company for him. He will get out of hearing as quickly as possible, and being of a rather decided character, as all good foxes are, will not wait to be tally-ho'd and screamed at by the vulgar, but goes away at once. The meets at Ivybridge on great occasions sometimes number three hundred. But there are laggards amongst them, and if the fox breaks quickly, they are not all up. The moorman, on his small lean thoroughbred-looking mare, with power in the right place, leads the way down what he is pleased to call a path, perpendicular, embossed with boulders, through a dense copse, into a ravine, at the bottom of which is a foaming river. He knows the crossing-place, and you must condescend to follow; not only that, you must descend at the same pace as he does, which is no condescension at all. In any other country this would look like a break-neck piece of business, but on Dartmoor it is only a common-place everyday transaction, and nobody ever breaks his neck. This is a Dartmoor cleave, coombe, or valley, cleft by the waters, and it is very beautiful. The stream is too large to be called a brook, but the trees nevertheless meet over it, and the dense mass of copse defies the fisherman. The moorman must be followed on the other side, for he knows the way out, and he must go to the moor as quickly as possible. He will tell you that there is not a moment to spare, and not to be in a hurry, which is very good advice, though it sounds ambiguous. He means that you must be as quick as you can be, but you must not hurry your horse; for if you impart your hurry to him and set his heart beating, he will not "show you the run." As for the moorman, he goes on at a perpetual easy, deliberate gallop. The hounds are ahead, he knows well, but he cannot afford to bustle his mare, and once on the moor he will get to their sterns somehow. He cares not who passes him, he has only one object in view, and that is to see the run which, if a good moor-run, will demand all his skill and horsemanship, added to the staying blood of his mare. It is hopeless to attempt crossing the few enclosures between the covert and the moor. The moorman scuttles up an unpromising unsportsmanlike-looking lane, and you had better put your pride in your pocket and do the same. Suddenly you emerge on the moor, and you have before you what looks like a vast expanse of fine turf short furze, and heather, backed, it is true, by dark-looking hills, with tors on their tops, and a suspicion of granite rocks scattered about; but where you are is ground fit for a racecourse. You are on high land; and, if you are so foolish as to look behind you, Plymouth Sound, with the ships at anchor, the Channel, and a lovely country, rich with meadow, woods, rivers, and pleasant-looking mansions, lies several hundred feet below. Thanks to the moorman, you find yourself on pretty good terms with the hounds, the high enclosures having hindered them a little; but now they are racing as hounds on Dartmoor only do race, with a straight-running fox before them, and under them the old primeval turf which has never known the plough, and a soil on which the gentle dews of heaven never cease to drop. This seems an exceedingly pleasant hunting country, and nothing can be easier than riding to hounds. It is still rising ground, but it does not look very steep, and now would be the time to ride at the tail of the pack; but you have been warned to keep your eye on the moorman, and you see him going on the same easy gallop as before, with his mare's ears pricked forward hearkening to the hounds. It is exactly the pace she can keep up for ever. The moorman kindly throws away his advice on young Ambition, who gallops past him on a hack. "Gently, young fellow," he says, in his own broadest Devonshire, "you'll beat your horse." "Oh! I'll take my guinea out of him," says Ambition, who has that sum to pay for his hack. "You've a-took nineteen and sixpence out of him already," says the moorman, which proves only too true, for in another furlong or two the poor hack hopelessly stops for good, and young Ambition has to get back to his mess at Plymouth, where he tells his brother officers what a beastly country Dartmoor is.

You are not long in getting over this fine ground and reaching the black-looking tors. The ground has been gradually rising, and most of the three hundred who had somehow got to the moor have tailed off. The scenery is very wild, and the enclosures are out of sight, except in the distance where the sun is smiling upon them. There is sound footing round the tors, but the high tableland is hopeless bog, from which trickle the streams that scoop out the deep coombes, and joining their forces form into rivers. Where the ground is sound it is studded with granite boulders, and between tor and tor there is a steep bit of rocky riding, with a brook in a bed of rocks at the bottom. The hounds are going at their best pace, and you must ride down over these rocks at your best pace, for down this hill, or precipice, if you like, is the chance you have to get on better terms with the pack. The moorman knows the best crossing-place, to which he has ridden rather faster than before, but still with none of that fatal hurry, down over rocks which would make a stranger's hair stand on end. But facing the hill opposite is a far more serious thing, and to ride up a hill properly so that your horse, who must be a stout one, can gallop when at the top, is the art of riding over Dartmoor to hounds. Many a horse will do the first hill gallantly, and perhaps the second; but the third is the stopper, and when you have got to the top of that and find that your horse can gallop, you may put him down as a Dartmoor hunter, and you may be sure he comes of a long line of sires of the best staying families in England. You may be very proud of your horse, but the moorman will ask you, "Can a' continny?" which, being interpreted, means, "Can he continue to gallop for ever?" If he cannot, his mane and his tail and all his other beauties are held in scorn. Having successfully followed the moorman up this first hill at exactly the right pace, no faster and no slower, you find yourself by no means too near the hounds, who are running over the bogs on your left faster than you ever saw hounds run before, and you have now to encounter the greatest difficulties that Dartmoor presents. Well may the Quorn man say, "This is no country for me." Nevertheless, it demands the finest horsemanship at your disposal, and the word fine here means "refined," for care of your horse and nursing his powers are indispensable requisites. No stranger can go here; you must know every inch of the country, or you must follow someone who does. There are three sorts of bog – the impassable, the just passable, and the sound, though deep – indistinguishable except by personal experience. This the moorman has; it has been the business of his life, and he has been in all of them. His mare is going her usual pace, which you now seem to think rather fast, with her ears pricked forward as before, listening to the hounds. He takes a very decided line, and soon gets on the jobber's path, on which drovers have driven their cattle for centuries, as sound ground in the midst of the bogs. He keeps the hounds well in sight and hearing by virtue of this path, but suddenly leaving it he rides down a boggy precipice with the inevitable granite, improving his pace a little, to the River Awne. It is the Awne in Dartmoor, but the Avon "in along." It is a bad river to cross, but he knows the best place, and half cheats the opposite hill by riding up a little coombe with a stream in it. The hounds have crossed about a quarter of a mile above, the worst of Dartmoor has been passed, and you are on the best galloping ground on its borders. The hounds are still going a terrific pace, and you must ride all you know. Your horse has just done his second hill, and the third is to come. You are on high land, and away on your right you can see the valleys and thick woodlands leading down to the Dart; beyond, the rich land, with Teignmouth and the Teign in the extreme distance. Before you, some way off the moor, lie Holne Chase and Buckland-on-the-Moor, two of the most lovely places in Devon, opposite one another, with the Dart rolling and roaring between

Oh, river Dart! oh, river Dart!
Every year thou dairn'st a heart.

You are not on a racecourse after all; there are small, deep coombes to cross, and as the hounds are going straight for Holne Moor, the moorman thinks Benjay Tor is his point (never, as a rule, ride to points), and he rides for the crossing-place over the brook which runs through that most lovely of all lovely fox coverts, Skaye, the deepest gorge of granite and the densest thicket of copse and gorse to be found anywhere, impenetrable even to the moorman. But the fox has heard Susan's tongue there, and he likes Benjay Tor better. Now comes the third hill down and up, steep, rocky, and trying, and the moorman is on Home Moor, with the heather up to his mare's knees and the blackcock flying about. The heather holds scent well, and the pace of the hounds is as good as ever, better it could not be, but it is high land, and there is a slope down to Benjay Tor with sound ground under the heather. If there is anything left in your horse, you can improve your pace, in the faith that no fox is such a fool as to scorn Benjay Tor. There you find yourself well up with the hounds, though you have never ridden a severer run in your life, but not the three hundred. A select few straggle up, and look very pretty with their red coats, off their horses, standing on the top of the tor. It is a rule with the moorman to get off his horse whenever there is nothing doing, to ease her spine, as he calls it. There speaks the good horseman. The fox has gone in, too deep in the granite for any terrier to fret him. It is a fox's "holt," and he gets air through the cracks in the rock. In his present state he could not breathe in an earth," hence the distinction. It would take a population of miners to get him out; and the huntsman, who is up, grumbles, for he thirsts for his blood. You secretly rejoice that he has saved that beautiful brush of his, with the long white tag at the end; and that his intelligent mask, with his bright eyes dimmed, is not dangling at the whip's saddle. You stand on the top of Benjay Tor, which is the granite crown of a high cliff hanging over the Dart, with a corresponding cliff – Sharpy Tor, on the opposite side. It is all dense copse and granite stretching down the steep banks of the Dart as it flows to Home Cot, Home Chase, and Buckland-on-the-Moor, "brawling," as the poet says, as it goes. Looking up stream, it is the same; but further up you see Dart Meet, where the two Darts, East and West, separate or join (as you like it); and in the background Dartmoor again appears – shall we say frowns? – looking black at you, with fine rugged tors, Belliver Tor, the chief, on his forehead. It is the finest spot in Devonshire, and, according to the moorman, the finest spot in the world. His mare looks as if another five miles or so of galloping would be a pleasure to her; but he says a cheery "Good-bye!" and goes off into the heart of the moor at a slow hound-trot, which often takes him twenty-five miles to covert with ease. He "knows by" a path with a good sandy bottom through the bogs to his snug home in a deep valley on the western side of the moor. You have seen Dartmoor, and you have had a lesson in riding. The last stave of the epic was sung by the moorman when he cried his "Whoo-hoop !" at Benjay Tor, in a scream that awakened all the echoes of all the hills.

"Further up you see Dartmeet, where the two Darts, East and West, separate or join." Dartmeet 1890.

In at the kill. An otter hunt in Devon c. 1910.

Chapter Thirteen

OTTER-HUNTING ON DARTMOOR

The otter is said to be the wildest animal hunted in this country. Most of the natural animals are more or less familiar with the appearance of man on earth. To their sorrow they are apt to meet him at every turn, for he with his domestic animals monopolises the land and drives them from their ancient inheritance. If Mr Henry George's doctrines were extended to animals in general, and not in so narrow a spirit limited to man, they would be most acceptable to a large majority of our fellow-creatures.

The habits of the otter afford him but very few opportunities of seeing the human form divine, and when he does see it, which must be in most cases at an otter-hunt, clothed in the costume affected by otter-hunters, it cannot seem to him at first sight "a thing of beauty," and is very far indeed from being "a joy for ever." There are many more otters in the world than mankind in general are at all aware of. As they do not see much of man, still less does man see of them. They frequent the coasts in large numbers, especially where rivers enter the sea, and where there are rocks. Being fishers by profession, they make excursions up the rivers to hunt the salmon and trout, not to mention the frog, which is a very delicate dish. They like a warm dry bed after their wet work, which they make in the banks of the river above water level, amongst rocks or the roots of large old trees, the only entrance often being under water. Here they put down their young, funny little things, mainly consisting of very thick skin and dense fur, in all seasons of the year (young otters have been found in every month of the year), and go out fishing until the otter-hunter comes to spoil their sport. Man is very wrath at the idea of an otter catching and eating salmon; but, as everybody knows, a spirit of fair play prevails among sportsmen, and as in the case of the fox, the only legitimate way of killing him is by an elaborate trial by jury, as it were, of foxhounds, with a scarlet huntsman, and blowing of horns, like trial by jury at the assizes – so there is only one legitimate way of killing an otter, all guns, traps, and other engines being held in scorn and indignantly stigmatised as unfair. The peculiar fairness of the legitimate method would not, however, be very striking to any one who did not know what chances it gave the otter to escape. The fact is, it takes a skilful huntsman and a good pack of hounds with terriers to find an otter in the first place, and kill him in the second. In the West of England the fox-hound is chiefly used to hunt the otter, and that fine picturesque otter-hound whose portrait Landseer loved to paint and painted so well with his long head, small eyes set close together, shaggy coat, and rushy stern, his deep bass tongue too freely given, fine nose, and patient style of hunting, is not much in vogue there. The dashing fox-hound is the fashion. He is handsome, a fine hunter, and the field know him, admire him, and like him. Well might the otters pray that the fashion may continue, for this dash of his saves many a life.

Otter-hunting can be seen in very good style on Dartmoor, on the river Dart. The hounds are taken in the middle of the summer to the "Saracen's Head," at Two Bridges, on the West Dart, in the heart of Dartmoor. The old original "Saracen's Head" was brought by the Bullers from the Crusades, and this is only a copy of it – a fastidious artist might say a rough copy – swinging in an iron frame over the door of an inn, and creaking all night when the rains and the winds come to help on the

"The hounds are taken in the middle of the summer to the Saracen's Head at Two Bridges." The Saracen's Head (on left), 1889.

rivers, a duty which they, as a rule, assiduously perform. For otter-hunting a time should be chosen when this duty has been somewhat neglected, and the rivers run light. The meet of the hounds should be early on a fine morning at Dart Meet, where the East and West Dart join, and the hounds should draw up the West Dart. The West Dart is much the finer river of the two; and, with its tributaries – the Cowsick, the Black-a-brook, the Cherry Brook, and the Swincombe – is the perfection of a Dartmoor river, flowing bright and rapid over a bed of granite boulders richly covered with moss and lichen, its banks bedecked with the ferns and wild flowers of the moor, and fringed with the bogmyrtle and withy. Water holds scent well, as not only otter-hunters, but stag-hunters, know; and the whiff so fragrant to the nose of the hound rises to the surface and floats down stream, calling forth his musical chant of praise. For this reason otter-hunters draw up stream, and before the lair of the otter is reached the welkin rings with the music of the pack. The otter has left his trail on the banks and on the stones where he has landed when fishing, his spur can be seen freshly printed on a sandy nook, and he is very likely to be found in a well-known and remarkably safe holt, as they call it in the West, about half a mile above Dart Meet, which he shares at times with foxes, though his access to it is under water, and theirs of course above. If he were but wise enough to stay here, he might defy his legitimate enemies to do their worst. But he knows not man and his little ways, and he has heard the unwonted strain of the hounds as they have been crying over his footsteps hard by. They mark him in his retreat, and the whole pack proclaim that he is in the otter's parlour, the strongest place on the river. It is in a large rock hanging over a deep, dark pool in a corner made by a turn in the river, with an old battered oaktree growing somehow from the midst, and backed by a confused jumble of granite blocks. The artist and the fisherman both admire this spot, though for totally different reasons, but the hunter likes it not, for he knows too well that if he runs the fox or the otter here his sport is over. A fox or an otter if run here is likely to stay; he has experienced the dangers and wickedness of the world at large but if found here in his quiet and repose he takes alarm at the unusual turmoil and incontinently bolts. The otter is known to have a way in under water, where no terrier can go, and he is so far safer than the fox. The most arduous otter-hunters, therefore, when the hounds mark, plunge up to their necks in the water to frighten him out with their otter-poles. He has long known the Dart as a quiet, peaceable, happy hunting-ground; and he makes the fatal mistake of bolting, little recking what a harrying awaits him for the next four hours. There immediately arises a yell of "Hoo-gaze!" the view halloo of the otter-hunter, probably an older English hunting halloo than tally ho! and the din of the hounds and terriers, the human scream, and the horn, like Bedlam broken loose, which he hears behind him, make him hurry up stream as best he may. The master of the hounds, if he knows his business, will now call for silence, and, taking out his watch, will give the otter what he calls a quarter of an hour's law. It is wonderful how fond sportsmen are of law; perhaps there is an affinity between prosecuting a case and pursuing a chase. He wants the otter to go well away from his parlour, and his object for the rest of the day will be to keep him out of it. If he is a real good sporting otter-hunter, he will tell his field that he wants his hounds to kill the otter without assistance from them; for in the West of England the vice of mobbing the otter is too common, with half the field in the water, hooting, yelling, poking with otter-poles, mixing the wrong scent, (their own) with the right, making the water muddy, and turning the river into a brawling brook with a vengeance. The true otter-hunter only wants his huntsman and whip, and perhaps a very knowing and trustworthy friend, besides himself, to help in hunting the otter with his hounds, and not with men. The master gives the chase a good quarter of an hour by the clock; and, leaving the unearthly, or perhaps too earthly, sounds behind him, the otter makes up stream as fast as he can go. It is surprising how far an otter can get in the time, but fear lends speed to his feet. Then begins the prettiest part of the sport. The hounds are laid on, they dash into the river, and instantly open in full cry. The water teams with the scent of the otter; but the deep pools, rapid stickles, and rocky boulders over which the river foams hinder the pace. There is ample time to admire the spirit-stirring and beautiful scene. The whole pack swimming a black-looking pool under a beetling Tor in full chorus; now and then an encouraging note on the horn; the echoes of the deep valley; the foaming and roaring Dart flowing down from above; the rich colour from the fern, the gorse, the heather, the moss, and the wild flowers; a few scattered weather-beaten oaks and fir-trees, and the stately Tors aloft, striking on the eye and ear, make one feel that otterhunting on Dartmoor is indeed a sport.

The Dart is a large river, for a Dartmoor stream, and presents many obstacles to the hounds; but they pursue the chase for some distance, and at length stop and mark, as they did before. The otter has got out of hearing, and has rested in a lair known to him under the riverbank. The terriers and an otter-pole dislodge him, and the sport becomes fast and furious. He is seen in all directions, sometimes apparently in two places at once, which makes the novice think there are two or three otters afoot; but it is only his quickness, and he dodges about amongst the boulders and under the banks in a manner that baffles all his foes, hound or man. "Hoogaze!" is now often heard, as one or another catches sight of him, and the field become very noisy and excited. It is still the object to run him up stream, whilst he now finds it easier to swim down. "Look out below" is therefore heard in the fine voice of the master. There is a trusty person he should be a very trusty person – some way down stream patiently watching a shallow stickle, where the otter must be seen if he passes. If he should get below this he must be turned up again, if possible. Suddenly the whole clamour ceases and silence prevails. The otter has mysteriously disappeared, no man or hound knows where, after the manner of otters, and he has to be fresh found. The master, a good sportsman and knowing in woodcraft, is in no hurry. There is too much scent in the water of various sorts, and he will be glad to pause until it has floated away. He takes his hounds down stream, and some of the field having unduly excited themselves vote it slow but he is nothing if he is not an otter-hunter, and his business is to kill the otter in a legitimate manner. Down stream, therefore, he goes with his hounds at his heels. The trusty man says the otter has not passed; but this makes no difference. Some way further down, with a wave of his hand, he sends all the hounds into the river again with a dash, and one or two challenge, upon which the novice pronounces the trusty man a fool; but they only speak on the surface-scent, which the current has washed into the bank, as the master knows well enough. They draw up stream again, pass the trusty man still at his post, and reach the spot where the otter vanished. The river is beautifully clear again, and an old hound marks. A good hour perhaps has been lost, or rather spent, since the otter disappeared, and here he has been in one of his under-water dry beds. He is routed out by otter-poles, and liveliness again prevails, especially when he takes to the land to get down stream by cutting off a sharp curve in the river-a way he has learnt in his frogging expeditions-and the hounds run him then like a fox. He is only too glad to plunge headlong into the river again, and he has reached it below the trusty man, who, however, goes down to the next shallow, and takes with him some others to turn the otter up from his safe parlour. They are hunting him now in a long deep pool, where he shifts from bank to bank, moving under water whilst the hounds swim above. He has a large supply of air in his lungs, which he vents as he uses it, and which floats to the surface in a series of bubbles. Otter-hunters call it his chain, and it follows him wherever he goes, betraying his track in the muddiest water. He craftily puts his nose, his nose only, up to get a fresh supply of air now and then, under a bush or behind a rock, and then owners of sharp eyes call "Hoo-gaze!" He finds himself in desperate straits, and he makes up his mind to go for his parlour at all hazards; but the hounds catch sight of him in the shallow of the trusty man, and the chase comes to an end. Otters are never speared in the West.

Some short time afterwards, one of the field who has behaved himself; pleased the master, and given the huntsman half-a-sovereign, will be seen in a waistcoat made of his beautiful thick skin and soft fur.

Thus may otter-hunting be followed on the West Dart on Dartmoor as a summer sport, amidst fine wild scenery and in jovial company.

Envoi

HUNTING IN THE MOOR COUNTRY*

When we first hear of Dartmoor it is as a hunting-ground of the King, and although Royalty does not now join in the chase over its bare hills and through its rocky glens, and the hounds no longer rouse the lordly stag from the border coverts, it is still, as it has been through the centuries, the scene of many an exhilarating run, and the silence of the waste is yet often broken by the sound of the huntsman's horn.

The connection of Dartmoor with the chase in early times is frequently shown in ancient land tenures, and there are also allusions in various documents to the deer upon it. The lands of David of Sciredun were held by him conditionally upon his finding two arrows when the King hunted on Dartmoor; Odo Arch and Walter de Bromhall held lands in Droscumb subject to finding a bow and three arrows; and two arrows and an oat cake were also to be supplied by William de Albemarle in return for his manor of Loston.

The Forest perambulators of 1609 report that William Chastie "kild a stagge with a pece or gun" on Dartmoor, for Sir Thomas Wise, of Sydenham. In the Pipe Rolls it is set forth how one Nicholas Payne, being appointed "to make provycon of fresh meate" for the use of Prince Charles, son of James I, on his homeward voyage from Spain, in 1623, sent out, among other things, "three stagges and fower buckes from the foreste of Dartmore"; in 1627 several deponents in a suit in which the rector of Lydford was the defendant, refer to the deer, which do not then appear to have been very abundant, and the Rev. George Lyde, vicar of

*Originally appearing in One Hundred Years on Dartmoor by William Crossing, 1901.

Widecombe at the time of the great storm in 1638, also mentions them in a poem that he has left us.

In the 18th century deer did such injury to the crops on the borders of the Moor in the neighbourhood of Tavistock, that, as we learn from Mrs. Bray, the farmers petitioned the Duke of Bedford to get rid of them, and his grace accordingly sent his staghounds down from Woburn, and it is said the deer were extirpated. But Miss Rachel Evans in her book on "Tavistock and Its Vicinity" says, though we do not know on what authority, that the last herd of deer (presumably in that district) was driven during a hard winter on to the frozen surface of the Tamar, and the animals were drowned by the breaking of the ice. This was the work of farmers, whose motives, however, were not only to prevent further havoc being wrought in their fields, but also to vent their spleen against the master of the hounds to whom they had taken a dislike. Miss Evans states that the event occurred about fifty years before she wrote, which was in 1846.

But, as far as recorded, 1780 was the year in which the last deer was killed by hounds on Dartmoor, for information relative to which subject we are indebted to Mr. F. Fearnley Tanner. We learn from him that in the latter part of the 17th century kennels were built at the old Manor House of Brook, between Buckfastleigh and Holne (the house bears the date 1656, but this was a restoration only) and a regular pack of stout, deeply-flewed hounds – tradition says of the bloodhound type – was kept for staghunting.

Previous to this red deer were hunted on Dartmoor not by an organised pack, but rather as occasion offered. In the entrance hall of Brook are eight sets of antlers, and the latest in date has this inscription under it: "This stag was roused in Brook Wood, and killed after a very fine chase of $5\frac{1}{2}$ hours, by the hounds of Bidlake Herring, Esq., September 17th, 1780."

Deer do not, however, seem to have entirely

disappeared from Dartmoor till some time after the above date, if Cooke is correct. Writing about 1805, he says that they were then nearly exterminated, but that some from the Moor had entered Boringdon Park within a few years previously, and had remained there with the fallow deer during several months.

But stragglers from the North of Devon have since occasionally visited the Moor. Mrs. Bray, writing in 1832, mentions that such was the case in her neighbourhood, and in Bellamy's "Natural History of South Devon" it is stated that deer had sometimes been observed in the vicinity of Ashburton, and that one was hunted near that town about 1836. In December, 1882, a stag was found by the Modbury Harriers at Leigh Wood, near Gara Bridge, on the Avon. It was run to Stowford Cleaves, above Ivybridge, and thence for some distance across the Moor, being eventually lost near Meavy. Within the past nine years deer have been seen in Buckland Woods, on the Dart; also on Hembury, in the same neighbourhood, and on the side of Cosdon, in the north of Dartmoor. Mr. C. F. Burnard also saw one a few years ago while fishing near Swincombe, in the heart of the Moor.

In 1892 two hinds and a fawn, which had been seen for some time previously in Buckland Woods, were roused by the Dart Vale Harriers, and driven up the Widecombe Valley, and deer have also been observed there more recently. In 1898, several having harboured in these woods, which belong to Mr. Bastard, a revival of staghunting on Dartmoor was attempted. Sir John Amory's staghounds were brought down, and a meet took place at Welstor Cross, about two miles from Ashburton. But the hopes which had been formed were doomed to disappointment. A numerous field assembled, but no deer could be found, although one old resident affirmed that stags had been in the coverts for ten years. Mr. Ian Amory, the Master of the staghounds, tried the woods on each side of the Dart, but there was no result, and thus the latest chapter in the history of hunting the red deer on Dartmoor ended.

The fox, like the deer, has also been hunted for a considerable time on Dartmoor, and has now usurped the place of the latter in the chase. He is mentioned among the animals hunted in the country watered by the Tavy, in an old poem called "Tavestock's Encomium," considered, according to Mrs. Bray, to have been written by a schoolmaster of that town in the latter part of the reign of Charles II.

But Masters of Hounds in the last century did not confine themselves to hunting Reynard solely. Mr. Arscott, of Tetcott, immortalised in the old Devonshire ballad, kept no less than three packs – staghounds, foxhounds, and harriers – his country extending over the Moors of Holsworthy and Broadbury. This wild district was in his time almost one with Dartmoor, and, indeed, for some period subsequently.

From Cooke's "Topographical Survey of Devon" we learn that in the early years of the 19th century the country north of Tavistock and towards Launceston, and also eastward to the immediate environs of Okehampton, was one great stretch of Moorland, extending from the skirts of Dartmoor to the uncultivated hills of Cornwall; for although the tract was strewed with plots of reclaimed land, there was no regular line of separation between the two upland regions.

In the days of Arscott, of Tetcott, the management of a pack of hounds was not quite the same thing it is today. Mr. C. A. Harris, in his "Letters on the Foxhounds of Devonshire," tells us that the value of an intelligent whipper-in was ignored, and that "a burly groom, with a powerful arm to crack a hunting-whip of the size and shape of a flail," was deemed all sufficient. There was a coarseness, too, among the hunting men of that time to which those of the present day are happily strangers. Then "sportsmen of degree sat down to dinner in greasy leather breeches, tattered slippers, and with loosened shirt collars, to facilitate the process of deglutition"; and with such an example set them it is scarcely to be wondered at that "brutality in word and deed – and an incessant noise – characterised the old Devonshire huntsman and his assistant." Social and educational progress has left all this behind.

The first Dartmoor fox of which we have any record in the 19th century was unseen – only his footprints being observable, which he had left, not on the sands of time, but on the black, peaty bottom of Cranmere Pool, where they were discovered by Mr. E. A. Bray in September, 1802. Cranmere, though still called a pool, is now merely a hollow in the midst of the fen, the greater part of the bottom of which is covered with coarse vegetation, and it is incapable of holding water, there being a breach in the bank on the northern edge. The cause of the latter is explained in various ways, one being that the bank was dug through in consequence of a hunted fox having gone to earth there. However this may be, it would appear that the breach was made subsequently to Mr. Bray's visit, for though he remarks that the pool was then dry, he speaks of its capability of holding water to a depth of six or eight feet.

Down to less than a hundred years ago packs of hounds seem to have been very numerous, but were kept on an entirely different plan from that of modern days. In the records of Fardel Manor, on the southern confines of the Moor, and now the property of Mr. J. D. Pode, of Slade, there is evidence of this, and Mr. Pode states that it appears that every house of any pretension in that neighbourhood – Delamore, Blachford, Fardel, Slade, Goodamoor – had its pack of hounds. There is no doubt that the records of other manors on the Moorland borders would show a similar state of things.

The only pack of hounds kept within the Forest of which we have any report was, according to a story still current in the neighbourhood, kennelled at Babeny, and belonged to Sir John Rogers, of Blachford. That Sir John was connected with that place is certain, for Mr. Robert Burnard has ascertained that he was admitted tenant of two ancient tenements there on the 17th March, 1814. But what appears strange is that he did not hold them, for almost immediately after his admission he surrendered them to another. Sir John finds a place in a lyrical account of a chase and a dinner of the Chulmleigh Hunt Club, in the year above-named, written by Mr. George Templer.

In addition to the fox, the hare and the otter are also hunted on Dartmoor, its early traditions being thus well maintained.

For a considerable time the Moor country has been partitioned for hunting purposes into four districts, but these correspond only in a slight degree with the ancient quarters of the Forest. What for convenience sake may be termed the northern district, but which excludes much of the north quarter, at the same time taking in a considerable portion of the east quarter, belongs to the Mid Devon Hunt. It comprehends that portion of Northern Dartmoor lying to the eastward of the West Ockment, and of a line drawn by Kneeset to Cut Lane and the East Dart, which stream becomes the boundary to Post Bridge, where the Moreton road acts as a dividing line between it and the eastern district.

Until recently Mr. Hayter-Hames and Mr. Windham H. Holley were joint Masters of the Mid Devon Hounds; but the present Master is Mr. Gilbert Spiller, of Eaglehurst, Chagford. The hounds are kennelled at Holy Street, and not very far from the picturesque old mansion of that name. The country which they hunt comprises some of the very wildest on the whole of Dartmoor, including within its area the dreary recesses around East Dart Head and Cranmere, amid which, without a perfect knowledge of the district, it would be impossible for a rider to follow hounds. It is only in a few places that it becomes possible for horses to cross the great expanses of boggy land; hence the best thing for a stranger to do is to endeavour to follow some member of the field who, he is satisfied, knows the ground.

The Furlong Harriers also hunt this side of the Moor, the Master being Mr. William Bragg, whose family have kept hounds for a longer period than any other in the Dartmoor country, and probably in the whole of Devon. In the 17th century Mr. Bragg's ancestor (his great-grandfather once removed) had a few couple of hounds, and with others used to hunt the deer, fox, otter, and hare on the Moor. Notes on the hunting of that period made by this Dartmoor Nimrod, and going back to 1600, were unfortunately destroyed by fire a few years ago.

His son, the present Mr. Bragg's great-grandfather, also kept hounds in the first half of the 18th century, and his mantle fell upon his son, Mr. George Bragg, who formed a pack at Moretonhampstead in 1793. In 1822 he gave the hounds to the Rev. W. Clack, who kept them at the Rectory, and they were afterwards hunted by his son and Colonel Stevenson. Mr. Clack's son, who was an uncle of Mr. William Bragg, was for many years the rector of Moreton, and died there in December, 1900.

The pack was subsequently given up, and in 1857 Mr. Westlake took up his residence at Sandy Park, near Chagford and hunted the South Devon Hounds until 1865. After that Mr. Bragg's father and uncle kept a pack of harriers, and at the death of the former in 1869 the latter continued to hunt them, but changed the pack to foxhounds about 1878.

True to the traditions of his family, the present representative, who has kindly furnished us with these particulars, continues to keep harriers, and, known by the name of his estate – Furlong, in the parish of

Drewsteignton – this fine pack shows many a good day's sport among the wild hills and rocky combes of the old Moor.

That this keen sportsman should have a desire that his son should keep hounds after him is but natural, and none on the Chagford countryside would wish otherwise. But they will, nevertheless, continue to hope that the Furlong Harriers will know no other Master than their present one for a long while to come.

The eastern part of the Moor is hunted by the South Devon Hounds, their country lying south of the Moreton-road, and extending westward to the Dart, thus embracing the great ridge of Hameldon, the Widecombe valley, and the range of common land around Hey Tor.

The earliest Master of Hounds of note, hunting this district during the present century, was one who has been spoken of as the favoured and favourite sportsman, anywhere and everywhere, Mr. George Templer, of Stover. In conjunction with his friends, Mr. Harry Taylor and Mr. Russell, it is said that he brought hunting to a state of perfection such as has scarcely ever been attained. So perfect was his mode of tuition that each hound comprehended every inflection of his voice, every note of his horn and wave of his hand. He exhibited such a scientific control over them that sterner discipline was unnecessary to ensure their obedience. Mr. Templer also kept a pack of well-bred little beagles, known as the "Let 'em-alones," immortalised by their master in a poem called "The Chase," written by him in 1822.

Genial and kind, George Templer was beloved by all with whom he came in contact, but to his sporting friends, to whom he was best known, he especially endeared himself. On Mr. Templer giving up keeping hounds his country was hunted by Sir Walter Carew, to whom he gracefully and feelingly alludes in some verses addressed to his "Old Horn," and which were recited by him at a gathering of sportsmen, at Chulmleigh, the Hon. Newton Fellowes being in the chair. His treasured horn, his gallant hounds, his steed lying beneath the mountain heather, and his departed friends in their "deep and dreamless sleeping," were all remembered in those farewell verses, and when his voice ceased there was not one in that company of gallant followers of hounds in whose eye the tear-drop did not stand.

This district was also the scene of the operations of Tom French, of Widecombe, who early in the 19th century waged war against the foxes in this neighbourhood of his home. According to the Rev. E. W. L. Davies, the author of "Dartmoor Days," Mr. John Bulteel is said to have turned loose a number of French and English foxes on Dartmoor. The farmers around Widecombe suffering considerably from their depredations, it was decided that endeavours should be made to exterminate them, and to Tom French was the task entrusted. To this he applied himself diligently, hunting the "varmints" with a few hounds and terriers, and when, after a long time, he found that he had gained the end in view, he also discovered that he had acquired a great liking for the chase. There being now no further support from the farmers, Tom's occupation was gone, but he was still determined upon the gratification of his new taste. He soon became an ardent follower of hounds, and was always a great favourite with the gentlemen of the hunt.

Possibly the descendants of some of the animals which Tom French at first so ruthlessly pursued are still found on the Moor. At all events, the fox in the southern portion of Dartmoor is said to be of Continental extraction, and is often spoken of as a French fox. He is different in appearance from the fox of northern Dartmoor, being smaller and of a redder colour. Mr. C. A. Harris describes the Moor fox of the latter district as high on leg, wiry, and powerful; a most redoubtable customer to meet at any time and an animal unknown to the eastward. "He is not to be handled after a thirty minutes' burst, but requires a long, stern chase at very great speed."

As pointed out in the chapter on wild quadrupeds in Rowe's "Perambulation," "the necessity for travelling long distances and the rough climate has led, by the survival of the fittest, in the matter of foxes, to the formation of almost a special breed in the Dartmoor highlands, having distinct peculiarities." Among hunting men this fox is known as the Dartmoor greyhound, and the fox of Broadbury, the country of Arscott, of Tetcott, as the Broadbury tiger.

The South Devon Hounds are hunted in a double pack, and the Masters are Mr. W. M. G. Singer and Mr. Robert Vicary. Members of this hunt will long remember James Collings, who for fourteen years acted as huntsman, and who was unfortunately killed while endeavouring to unearth a fox in Buckland Woods in December, 1898.

The Ashburton Harriers and the Dart Vale Harriers hunt the Moor country around Widecombe and Holne, and both packs are exceedingly popular. Mr. G. Standish Jackson is the Master of the former, and Mr. W. Phillips the Master of the latter. Mr. Phillips took charge of the pack in 1900, in succession to Mr. T. Maye, who had hunted the country for a considerable time.

The annual hunt weeks in connection with these packs bring together a large number of sportsmen from different parts of the county, as well as from Cornwall. On the finishing day of the Ashburton Week, in March of 1900, grand sport was witnessed, and the hunt dinner was afterwards held at the Globe Hotel, Ashburton.

During the Dartmoor Week the head-quarters of the hunt are at the Duchy Hotel, Princetown, and the Dart Vale Harriers meet in the immediate neighbourhood two days out of the four over which the assemblage extends, alternately with another pack – usually Mr. Netherton's. This pleasant fixture takes place in the month of April, and on the concluding day, the Friday, the meet is always at Bellaford Tor, and forms the great holiday of the year for the Dartmoor folk. It is invariably numerously attended, hundreds of visitors flocking to the tor. At this annual picnic on old "Bellever," in 1901, the field was probably the largest ever known there. It was considered that fully a thousand persons were present, more than five hundred of them being mounted, while vehicles of every description were to be seen on the slopes around the tor.

Handled by George Perry, the huntsman, the harriers showed splendid sport. At one time during the day the pack divided, five and a half couple hunting one hare, and the remainder of the pack giving their attention to another. Both were run into, a circumstance never before known in the annals of the Dart Vale Hunt.

In an account of the hunting on this side of the Moor, brief though it be, it is impossible to omit mention of "the happy Brimps' meetings," so charmingly described in the Rev. E. W. L. Davies' poem of "Dartmoor Days." At that place, "a hall of no pretence or fame," a joyous set, numbering among them some of the most famous sportsmen of the time, were, years ago, wont to resort. The days were passed in the pleasures of the chase, and each evening, when the grim old Moor was wrapped in darkness, witnessed a cheerful gathering round the glowing peat.

The south quarter of the Forest and the commons bordering upon it are included in the country of the Dartmoor Hounds, the present Master of which is Mr. William Coryton, of Highlands, Ivybridge, and the hounds are kennelled at Woodlands, which is not far distant. Prior to about 1828 this country was hunted by Mr. Pode, of Slade, and on that gentleman giving up keeping hounds, it was transferred to Mr. John King, of

Fowlecombe, and Mr. John Bulteel, of Lyneham. The former, a shrewd and observant sportsman, who well knew the nature and habits of the fox, died at the age of 73, in his saddle, on Dartmoor. His friend, Mr. George Templer, had, in a poem given him the title of "King of the West," and by this he was long known in the county. His association with Mr. Bulteel was only of a temporary nature, and the latter continued to hunt the country alone.

The mainstay of the Lyneham Hounds, as we learn from Mr. C. A. Harris, was Mr. Charles Trelawny, and he at length became Mr. Bulteel's successor. None among the lovers of the chase in the Westcountry have been more widely known than Mr. Trelawny – the Squire, as he was always termed. For years he was a familiar figure in the streets of Plymouth, and like another veteran, Mr. J. H. Newcombe, lessee of the Theatre Royal, might often have been seen, with bespattered tops and buckskins, riding slowly through the town at the close of a day's hunting.

Men who knew nothing whatever of field sports took some sort of an interest in the achievements of Mr. Trelawny's Hounds, impelled thereto by the personal popularity of their owner. When he became a master of foxhounds, hunting in that part of South Devon over which his country extended appeared to be on the decline. An authority has stated that he was the only man who had a chance to avert this. That he did so is now a matter of history, and the epoch of the Squire will always rank as one of the most popular in the annals of hunting in the West.

Of that other ardent follower of hounds, Mr. J. R. Newcombe, the memory is also yet green. Tough and agile as a youth almost to the last, the longest day's run on Dartmoor could not tire him. Often when billed to appear on his own stage has he ridden direct from the field to the theatre, and resigning his horse to the care of

John Blower, hastened to his dressing-room, and within a very short time bounded on to the boards, to all appearances as fresh as though he had been taking his ease during the day, instead of having spent it in the saddle. The effects of rain or snow never laid him up or caused him to disappoint an audience. A closely-fitting suit of chamois leather worn next the skin, and a strong constitution, enabled him to defy the bitterest Moorland storm, and to regularly appear for many years in the hunting-field and on the stage.

On Mr. Trelawny relinquishing the hounds in 1874 the country was hunted by Captain Munro, and also by Admiral Parker, of Delamore, and subsequently by Mr. William Coryton, the pack being appropriately named the Dartmoor Hounds. That the district should possess a Master of hounds so universally popular as he has become is a matter for congratulation. Mr. Coryton not only worthily maintains the reputation of his family as true sportsmen, but also the traditions that cluster round the country over which he has assumed the management.

It has, however, lately been found necessary to reduce the number of hunting days to two a week, and twenty-three and a half couple of hounds from the Dartmoor kennel were consequently sold in May, 1901, at Rugby. The entered hounds averaged twenty-two guineas a couple, and the unentered fifteen guineas a couple, the total amount realised being four hundred and fifty guineas.

The Modbury Harriers, the Master of which is Mr. W. Gage Hodge, sometimes hunt the southern borders of the Moor, the annual meet on Boxing-day at the Western Beacon, above Ivybridge, always drawing a numerous field, and being regarded in the neighbourhood as a holiday event. The south-western part of Dartmoor was formerly hunted by the Roborough Harriers, the Master being Mr. King, who, however, relinquished them about

1867. Part of the same country is now hunted by Mr. Sperling's harriers.

The Dartmoor Otter Hounds are also kept in the southern country – at Glazebrook, near South Brent, and, under the Mastership of Major Green, have become extremely popular. They can claim to be the oldest existing pack of otter hounds in Devonshire, and probably in England.

The originator was Mr. Pode, mentioned above in connection with the pack from which has sprung the present Dartmoor Foxhounds. With that pack he also hunted the otter, and this was continued to be done by Mr. Bulteel, Mr. Trelawny, and their successors. But during the Mastership of Admiral Parker the otter hunt was separated from the fox hunt, Mr. Gage Hodge becoming Master of the former. He soon revived the old glories, killing seventeen otters in his first season. At his death in 1892 he was succeeded by the present Master.

The country lying to the westward of that of the Mid-Devon Hunt, and bounded on the south by the road running from Post Bridge to the borders of the Moor beyond Princetown, is hunted by Mr. S. Adams, Master of the Lamerton Hounds. Mr. Bray, father of the Rev. E. A. Bray, used many years ago to hunt a part of this district, keeping a pack of hounds at Fitzford. Subsequently Mr. Morgan, of Woodovis, hunted the Tavistock country, and was known as a keen sportsman. When age crept upon him, and he found himself unable any longer to ride to hounds, he was wont to be driven to the meets, and then to certain points of vantage, in order that he might see, if possible, something of what the hounds were doing.

At his death Mr. Henry Deacon consented to hunt the country, also taking over that which belonged to Mr. Newton, of Bridestowe. He was associated with his brother James, and they are both still well remembered in the district. Mr. Deacon was a daring rider, and an excellent judge of what a hound should be. But though he performed his duties in a manner worthy of the highest praise, and exhibited a most liberal spirit, he did not receive that support which his efforts deserved. Foxes were destroyed everywhere, more than one hundred having been killed in four parishes within fifteen months, and this at length determined Mr. Deacon to resign the country, which he did in 1859.

Mr. Deacon was succeeded by Mr. William Leaman, who, in conjunction with his twin brother Thomas, hunted the country for some years, and both had the well-deserved reputation of being skilful and experienced sportsmen. Mr. Leaman received the firm support of the Duke of Bedford and Mr. Carpenter, of Mount Tavy, as well as of a number of other landowners, and continued to hunt the hounds until his death.

Colonel Deakin, of Werrington Park, then assumed the Mastership, but owing to a misunderstanding with respect to the limits of his country, did not continue to hold it very long, and the management then devolved upon Mr. Lobb, of Lawhitton.

Subsequently the Mastership was taken over by Mr. Reginald Kelly, of Kelly, Mr. Lobb still continuing to act as huntsman. From Mr. Kelly the hounds passed to his nephew, Mr. Sperling, who also kept a pack of harriers. The latter he still hunts, and his "little beauties", always attract a good field, and, under the guidance of the huntsman, Tom Bickle, never fail to render a good account of themselves. A few years ago Mr. Sperling resigned the Mastership of the Lamerton Hunt, which, however, has found a worthy successor in Mr. Adams.

To enumerate those noted among the sportsmen of Devonshire who hunted on Dartmoor during the 19th century is here impossible; but we cannot refrain from mentioning a few whose steeds have pressed the turf of the wild uplands. Their memories cluster round the tors of the Forest; their names seem to be borne upon the winds that stir the mountain heather. On a block of granite by the bank of the Avon, on Brent Moor, are graven the names of four worthies of the hunting field – Bulteel, Trelawny, Paul Treby, and Carew. We have already mentioned others; let us add those of "Gallant Tom Phillips," "Old Sarum," Sir Arthur Chichester, Sir Henry Seale, J. Morth Woollcombe, Captain Fortescue, "Otter" Davis, a parson of Halwell, who about 1830 kept a rough pack of hounds with which he hunted otters and all else, and "Passen Rissell," whose breed of fox terriers has attained a universal fame. Among huntsmen the names of John Roberts, Crocker, Limpetty, and Boxall will not soon he forgotten; Dartmoor may know their equals, but not their superiors.

By some the outlook for hunting in the Moor country has been considered to be a somewhat gloomy one, but others there are who do not perceive any indications of decay. On the contrary, they see the sport growing more and more in favour, with no lack of the support required, and, except in a few instances, a desire on the part of farmers for its continuance. The Dartmoor Sportsmen's Association does much to bring in friendly relationship the farmer and the sportsman, and to such an extent as to be rapidly including the first within the ranks of the last.

That which has been associated for centuries with Dartmoor is associated with it still, and unless Englishmen cease to be what they are at present it will be many a long year before the huntsman's horn shall cease to sound among the tors of the ancient Forest.